American Music Makers

AN INTRODUCTION TO AMERICAN COMPOSERS

American Music Makers

AN INTRODUCTION TO AMERICAN COMPOSERS

JANET NICHOLS

WALKER AND **COMPANY** **NEW YORK**

Copyright © 1990 by Janet Nichols

First published in the United States of America in 1990
by Walker Publishing Company, Inc.

Published simultaneously in Canada by Thomas Allen & Son
Canada, Limited, Markham, Ontario

Library of Congress Cataloging-in-Publication Data
Nichols, Janet
American music makers : an introduction to American composers / by Janet Nichols.
ISBN 0-8027-6957-8. — ISBN 0-8027-6958-6 (lib. bdg.)
1. Composers—United States—Biography. I. Title.
ML390.N58 1990
780'.92'273—dc20
[B]   90-11924
CIP
MN

To my children,
Caitlin and Sean,
With love

TABLE OF CONTENTS

ACKNOWLEDGMENTS

I wish to thank my agent, Diana Finch, and editor, Bebe Willoughby, for their support and guidance in turning my manuscript into a published book.

I am especially grateful to Milton Babbitt, George Crumb, Philip Glass, and Steve Reich for their cooperation and the assistance they gave me as I wrote their respective chapters.

Thanks to Billie Bandermann who assisted me in the research on Ives; to the librarians at the Menlo Park City Library who granted me access to the unpublished papers in the Henry Cowell Archive; to the librarians at the Centerville Branch of the Fremont City Library who placed in my hands every book I requested, whether or not they found it in their own system; and to Helene Cann of Outward Visions, Kendall Crilly of the Charles Ives Archive at Yale University, Susan Endrizzi of California Artists Management, Barbara Sawka of the Stanford Archive of Recorded Sound, and Paul Williams of Dunvagen Music—all of whom directed me toward information I needed.

I send, with love, a special thank you to Timothy Lynch, my listening partner and best friend, whose expertise in new music and whose generous nature granted me the luxury of having an in-house consultant on this project.

FOREWORD

Most people think all music played in recitals and concerts was written by European composers two hundred years ago. There is, however, an extension of classical music in the United States, and some of its contributors are composing new music today. Americans have always had their own ways of doing things and composers are no exception. Louis Moreau Gottschalk spiced his music with the Creole flavor of his childhood in New Orleans; Edward MacDowell was moved by the drum beat of Native Americans; George Gershwin got his start in Tin Pan Alley and went on to write one of America's greatest operas; Ruth Crawford Seeger mined the rich vein of American folk music and Milton Babbitt pioneered new ways to organize sound through electronics.

American music is a vast subject, and the hardest part about writing a book like this is deciding what to include. I chose to explore ten composers rather than gloss over many more. Each chapter includes a brief biography and a description of some of the composer's most important works.

All the composers in this book were born in the United States. Other American composers were born in Central and South America and still others were from foreign countries and obtained U.S. citizenship later in life. The composers that I did not include are not necessarily less important than the ones I chose to write about.

I would like to pay tribute to some of the composers I did not include in *American Music Makers* by mentioning them here. Those born in the United States include: John Adams, Samuel Barber, Leonard Bernstein, John Cage, Elliott Carter, Aaron Copland, Norman Dello Joio, Vivian Fine, Marion Gideon, Percy Grainger, Charles Griffes, Roy Harris, Lou Harrison, Harry Partch, Vincent Persichetti, Terry Riley, Ned Rorem, Carl Ruggles, Roger Sessions, William Grant Still, Morton Subotnick, Virgil Thomson, Joan Tower, Ralph Vaughan Williams, Charles Wuorinen, and Ellen Taaffe Zwilich. Some Central American composers are: Carlos Chavez, Alberto Ginastera, and Hector Villa-Lobos. Naturalized U.S. composers include: Ernest Bloch, Paul Hindemith, Gian Carlo Menotti, Arnold Schoenberg, Igor Stravinsky, and Edgard Varèse. I hope to write about some of these other American composers in the future.

This book is meant to be an introduction to music of the "New World." May it open up to you a whole new world of sound.

American Music Makers

AN INTRODUCTION TO AMERICAN COMPOSERS

Louis Moreau Gottschalk
Library of Congress

Chapter One
LOUIS MOREAU GOTTSCHALK
(1829–1869)

◆

Louis Moreau Gottschalk was a very talented little boy. At age three he could play on the piano songs that he heard his mother sing. At seven he was the substitute organist at the Cathedral of St. Louis in New Orleans, even though his legs were too short to reach the pedals. When he was ten years old, he played his first concert before a large audience. Two years later, his piano teacher told his parents that he couldn't teach him anything more. The teacher thought the boy should continue his study in Europe.

Mr. and Mrs. Gottschalk doted over the oldest of their seven children, whom they always called Moreau. They wanted him to get the best musical education, but they didn't want him to travel so far away. They were afraid he would be homesick. The Gottschalks lived in "The French Quarter" of New Orleans. Moreau was born on May 8, 1829, only 26 years after the United States bought the Louisiana Purchase from France. That made New Orleans seem more French than American. The Gottschalks spoke French and English in their home. Moreau's mother was creole, a descendant of French settlers, and his father was an English-born businessman who could speak eight languages. They decided Moreau should study in Paris and live with his great aunt, the Marquise de la Grange.

Moreau made the long journey across the Atlantic Ocean without any of his family. Five years would pass before his mother and brothers and sisters would join him in Europe. Moreau was very close to his family and missed them very much. But that was only one of his problems.

When Moreau applied for admission to the Paris Conservatory, the director of piano classes, Pierre Zimmerman, would not even listen to him play. "This is no place for Americans," he said. "America is a land of steam engines, a country of railroads, but not musicians."

It was true that no important musician or composer had been born in America; however, Moreau didn't see any reason why he couldn't be the first. At that time the piano was the most popular instrument in Europe. There were over twenty thousand piano teachers living in Paris alone. Moreau was certain that one of them could help prepare him for a career as a concert pianist.

He took lessons from Charles Halle and then Camille Stamaty.

After studying and practicing very hard for two years, Moreau gave his first concert in April of 1845. In those days, young musicians were not introduced to the public in the large concert halls. Instead, aristocrats invited them to play in the rooms of their palaces. These rooms were called salons. Although Moreau didn't get paid for his first concert, he performed at an important place—the Salon Pleyel. He played Chopin's E Minor Concerto while the composer listened in the audience. Afterwards, Chopin took his hand and told him that he would soon be "king of pianists." Moreau was very happy. He thought that that one compliment was much better than a degree from the Paris Conservatory.

Gottschalk didn't want to play only the music of others. At age fifteen he began to write his own compositions. Instead of trying to imitate the great works of Beethoven and Chopin, however, Gottschalk drew musical ideas from the sounds of his childhood.

He remembered the black slaves dancing the Bamboula on Sunday afternoons at Place Congo, which was located two blocks from his home in New Orleans. A drummer would play on an empty cask, using beef-bones for drumsticks. The women dancers, wearing brightly colored calico cloth, stamped their bare feet and chanted songs from their native Africa. The male dancers tied bits of tin to their ankles that rattled as their feet moved. The Bamboula started slow, then got faster and faster.

In his composition *Bamboula*, Gottschalk combined a Creole folk melody called "When That 'Tater's Cooked Don't You Eat It Up!" with the syncopated rhythms of the African dance. The piece opens with the melody, accompanied by heavy bass notes that thump like the bare feet of the dancers. This is followed by two more tunes—one is dancelike and the other is dreamy. After a section of cascading flourishes, the main melody returns in a sparkling shower of rapid repeated notes. *Bamboula* is exciting to hear and difficult to play.

In another early composition, *The Banjo*, Gottschalk recalled the American minstrel shows he saw when he was a boy. In these performances, traveling musicians blackened their faces with burnt cork and sang American songs, including works by Stephen Foster. They played banjos and tambourines, danced, and told jokes. For *The Banjo*, Gottschalk wrote a tune that is very much like "Camptown Races," and accompanied it with banjo plucking and strumming figures that sound quite unusual on the piano. The tempo grows faster and faster until the piece ends in a dazzling blur of sound.

When Gottschalk felt ready to charge admission to his concerts, he first toured the small towns and cities of France before returning to Paris. He was successful wherever he played. The Europeans were fascinated with anything faraway and exotic. They knew very little about American culture and had never heard anything like Gottschalk's music. The famous composer and critic, Hector Berlioz, wrote, "Mr. Gottschalk was born in America, whence he has brought a host of curious chants from the Creoles and Negroes; he has made from them the themes of his most delicious compositions." When Gottschalk acquired a French publisher for his music, his birth place became an important selling point. After his name on all his early compositions is the phrase, "of Louisiana."

In contrast to the brashness of his compositions, Gottschalk's manners were refined and his French was perfect. This delighted his public, especially the ladies. He was also very handsome, having chestnut hair and dreamy blue eyes. He was so pale and delicate-looking that his listeners were oftentimes surprised by his powerful piano technique. In describing it, critics choose phrases like "his golden touch," "cascades of pearls," and "glittering star dust." Gottschalk expended so much energy in his performances that they left him drained and sickly. Once, after a concert in Geneva, a hefty Swiss maiden threw a cloak over his head and carried him away on her shoulder. Gottschalk was so weak that he was unable to resist. When the story appeared in the newspapers the following day, Gottschalk was so embarrassed that he didn't finish his Swiss tour.

In 1851, Queen Isabella I of Spain asked Gottschalk to play at her palace. He accepted the invitation and ended up staying in her country for eighteen months. Gottschalk performed in the small provinces of Spain as well as the big cities. Usually he performed his own compositions, though occasionally he played Chopin and Beethoven.

Gottschalk composed a number of pieces while in Spain, using native tunes, rhythms, and dances. His most famous Spanish piece is *The Siege of Saragossa*, written for ten pianos and first performed in Madrid on June 28, 1852. Most compositions require only one piano and, rarely, two. Ten pianos produce quite a racket and take up a lot of room. Berlioz had made such "monster-concerts" popular in Europe, and this was probably the first one Gottschalk attempted. Unfortunately, the music for *The Siege of Saragossa* has been lost. We know, however, that it was based on the *jota*, a rapid Spanish dance in triple meter accompanied by castanets. Gottschalk's concert was a smashing success. After the performance, a huge crowd followed him to his hotel, including two bands that serenaded him. The next day, the most famous matador in Spain sent Gottschalk his jewel-studded sword.

Queen Isabella decorated Gottschalk with a medal and he was a hit everywhere he went in Spain. It seemed that all the Spanish people loved him, except, perhaps, the court pianist, who slammed a carriage door on Gottschalk's hand. The pianist insisted it was an accident, but Gottschalk suspected that it was done in a fit of jealousy. It took three months for the hand to heal. Afterward, Gottschalk claimed that it was stronger than ever.

After his tour of Spain, Gottschalk visited his family in Paris for several weeks. In December of 1852, he set sail to America. He never saw his mother and most of his brothers and sisters again. He had intentions of returning to Europe, but never did. Perhaps it was just as well. Gottschalk was a flashy pianist capable of lightning-fast finger gymnastics. This style of playing would soon go out of fashion in Europe, to be replaced by the soulfulness of Clara Schumann. Schumann and other pianists felt that music should stir deep feelings in listeners instead of merely entertaining them. Maybe Gottschalk sensed it was time to return to his own country.

After a twenty-one-day voyage across the Atlantic, Gottschalk met his father in New York. After a brief rest, he was faced with the chore of winning over his own countrymen. Though his American birth was not at all remarkable on this side of the ocean, his European training was. Unfortunately, Gottschalk started a tradition which became a curse on succeeding generations. Many American musicians who wished to gain prestige felt they had to study in Europe, even though our own country has many fine music schools.

Gottschalk played several concerts in New York. The audience and critics hailed him, but his numerous expenses resulted in a loss of $2400. The great circus ringmaster, P.T. Barnum, offered him a large salary to tour the country under his management. In need of money, Gottschalk was tempted to seize the opportunity. However, his father convinced him that his music was more dignified than the shows that P.T. Barnum presented.

Gottschalk decided to go on his own concert tour. He was triumphant in his hometown of New Orleans, but was received cooly in Boston, where the audiences were more sophisticated.

One night, just before he was about to play a concert in Boston, he got word that his father had died. Gottschalk played the concert anyway, although it didn't go very well. Besides grieving the loss of his father, he was faced with paying off his father's large debts and supporting his family. He was able to raise some money by playing over eighty concerts in New York during the following season.

Gottschalk's mother died suddenly in Paris three years later. Her death caused him great sorrow. He was also nervous and exhausted from his rigorous concert schedule. He retreated to the lush tropics of the West Indies for a short rest and ended up staying there five years. During these years he composed little and played only a few concerts. Instead he began writing, in French, his famous diary, *Notes of a Pianist.*

Gottschalk used the diary as a traveling companion. In it, he revealed his disappointment over rude audiences and his happiness over his successes. He put down his thoughts about politics, religion, and customs. He described the landscape he viewed and the numerous people he met. The diary is a vivid account of life in the mid-1800s and proves that Gottschalk was as talented in writing as he was in composing.

On February 17, 1860, Gottschalk presented a monster-concert in Havana for which he wrote an opera and several orchestra works. His huge cast consisted of 102 singers, fifty drums, eighty trumpets, and many other musicians. The orchestra parts amounted to eight thousand pages of music, which had to be copied by hand. During the week before the concert, Gottschalk slept only two hours a night so that he could finish copying all the music. The concert was a huge success, but it left him exhausted.

The rest of Gottschalk's time in the West Indies was much more relaxed. In his diary he wrote, "I have roamed at random under the blue skies of the tropics . . . giving a concert wherever I found a piano, sleeping wherever the night overtook me—on the grass of the savanna, or under the palm-leaf roof of a tobacco-grower with whom I partook of a tortilla, coffee, and a banana."

Gottschalk also spent a few months with a mysterious young lady. "I forgot the world," he wrote in his diary, "and lived only for two large black eyes, which veiled themselves with tears whenever I spoke of beginning my vagabond course again." No one knows who the woman was nor why she didn't go with Gottschalk when he left the West Indies.

In February of 1862, Gottschalk knew it was time to get back to work. He had been gone from the musical centers of the world so long that several newspapers reported his death. Gottschalk thought this was funny. In his diary he wrote:

> *"I wish to speak of my death. This sad event took place at Santiago three months ago. I was carried off in three days by a frightful attack of black vomit; it is the newspaper* Savana la Grande *that tells it; but the* Revue de Villa Clara, *without doubt better informed, makes me succumb to an aneurism of the heart, which I much prefer, the aneurism being much more poetical than the vomit."*

While Gottschalk was in the West Indies, the Civil War had begun in the United States. Newspapers in Havana reported that all the theaters of New York were closed. "Can you think of giving concerts before a public that wants bread?" one of his Cuban friends asked him. Gottschalk was relieved to find the accounts he had heard were wrong—New York was just as prosperous as when he left it.

Still, the Civil War caused Gottschalk much grief. Being Southern, he was sympathetic toward his relatives and friends, but he sided with the North. He thought slavery was cruel and immoral. He had freed the three slaves his family owned just as soon as his father died, many years earlier. He was outraged that Southerners were fighting for their independence just so they could enslave others. He also thought it was a political error for the South to want to form a new country. In his diary he wrote, "In the nineteenth century, nationalities are no longer broken—the general movement tends to unification."

Gottschalk joined a troupe of musicians that was managed by Maurice Strakosch and included Carlotta Patti, one of the most famous singers of the time. Gottschalk bought two ten-foot Chickering grand pianos and had them shipped wherever the troupe performed. The musicians gave concerts in Cincinnati, Louisville, St. Louis, and Chicago. Then they headed toward Harrisburg, Pennsylvania—due to arrive at about the same time as the Southern army. Gottschalk suggested to Strakosch that people who were about to be attacked by the enemy might not be in the mood for a concert. Strakosch, however, was certain he could sell a great number of tickets in Harrisburg.

Riding on the train into the city, the musicians saw roads completely blocked by wagons filled with cargo. The people were trying to get supplies out of Harrisburg so that they wouldn't be captured and burned by the rebels. Suddenly, the train stopped in the middle of the bridge over the raging Susquehanna River. The frightened passengers were not told why. After being held in suspense for over an hour, Gottschalk, Strakosch, and Madame Patti decided to walk to the station, which was only about two miles away. At the entrance to the depot they found trunks and cargo blocking the tracks. A locomotive, unable to stop in time, had tunneled through the heap. Contents of luggage and cargo were scattered everywhere. Gottschalk feared the worst for his valuable pianos, but found them in perfect condition in a far corner of the depot.

Harrisburg was in a state of panic. The merchants had closed their shops. Many people were fleeing in carriages and carts. The poor pushed their few possessions in wheelbarrows. Three thousand volunteers dug ditches from which soldiers would fight. Strakosch slapped his hands to his forehead and wailed, "Decidedly our concert is done for!" Gottschalk thought it was funny that with all the trouble, Strakosch still felt a canceled concert was the worst thing that could happen. The next day, the troupe of musicians boarded a train that carried two thousand people, who were packed like sardines, out of Harrisburg. Ironically, the battle was never fought in Harrisburg. Just two weeks later the Battle of Gettysburg marked the beginning of the end of the Civil War.

Meanwhile, the troupe continued their tour up North. At each concert, Gottschalk tried to give his audiences what they wanted to hear. He soon learned that he couldn't please all the people all the time. Many of his pieces were too complicated for simple folks. Once when a woman requested "Home, Sweet Home," she did not recognize the tune because Gottschalk decorated it with so much fancy finger work. One Canadian farmer had never seen a grand piano and wondered what "the big tail" was for. Some other rural folks startled Gottschalk by whistling loudly when they liked his playing. Another audience remained completely silent. The pianist asked someone why the people didn't clap for him and learned that they were angry because the tickets had cost a whole dollar.

More sophisticated audiences complained that Gottschalk's music was trivial. Perhaps his severest critic was John S. Dwight of Boston, publisher of *Journal of Music*, the most important music magazine in America. Dwight criticized Gottschalk for not playing the classics. "Play some *real* music," he once advised. This hurt Gottschalk's feelings. He wrote in his diary, "I begin to regret having received from God the afflicting gift of being able to create. . . . Are Classics superior to all we accomplish? . . . If the apple is a fruit less delicate than the pineapple, you would wish that there should be no apples?"

Though Dwight knew a lot about music, Gottschalk

thought he was an ignorant fool. He proved this to himself by playing a joke on Dwight. At one of his concerts in Boston, Gottschalk played a little-known work by Beethoven and attached his own name to it in the printed program. Then he played one of his own works, which he credited to Beethoven. Just as expected, Dwight praised the supposed Beethoven and condemned Gottschalk's piece as the brash work of an amateur. Gottschalk then apologized to Dwight for what he called a printer's error and thanked him for the praise of his composition.

Gottschalk tried especially hard to please the ladies. Women adored Gottschalk, causing one historian to dub him "American's First's Matinee Idol." Just as young women swooned over Frank Sinatra in the

With his dreamy eyes and dazzling piano playing, Gottschalk often caused female fans to swoon
Library of Congress

1950s, The Beatles in the 1960s, and Michael Jackson more recently, so did their great-great-grandmothers swoon at the sight and sound of Gottschalk. Some young ladies even stormed the stage in pursuit of a lock of his hair. Gottschalk loved women as much as they loved him. He once said that pretty young ladies sitting in the front row caused him to play wrong notes.

The women's favorite piece was Gottschalk's "The Last Hope." It is a slow, sentimental composition written in a style known as salon music. It lacks the merit of *Bamboula* and *Banjo*. Gottschalk knew this, but that didn't stop him from playing it over and over. The front page of the sheet music for "The Last Hope" tells the story of a dear woman friend of Gottschalk's who was seriously ill. Fearing that she would die before seeing her only son one last time, she asks, "In pity, my dear Moreau, one little melody, the last hope!" Gottschalk supposedly sat down and composed "The Last Hope" on the spot and the woman died peacefully soon after. All the young ladies who listened to Gottschalk play "The Last Hope" knew this story because they had bought the sheet music and played and wept over it in their own parlors. Gottschalk found the music for sale in every town. If the town didn't have a music store, he found it in the stationery or shoe store. Gottschalk was able to pay off most of his father's debts with the royalties from "The Last Hope." He once commented that it swept the New World "like a plague."

The Union was another composition that was very successful both in Europe and in America. This piece is not an original work, but rather a medley of "The Star-Spangled Banner," "Yankee Doodle," and "Hail Columbia." The six-page introduction is so long it might tempt some modern-day listeners to giggle. Gottschalk greatly admired Abraham Lincoln and played "The Union" for him at a concert in Washington on March 24, 1864.

Of Lincoln, Gottschalk wrote, "Tall, thin, his back bent, his chest hollow, his arms excessively long, his cranelike legs, his enormous feet, the long frame whose disproportionate joints give him the appearance of a grapevine covered with clothes . . . Lincoln is remarkably ugly, but has an intelligent air, and his eyes have a remarkable expression of goodness and mildness . . . Lincoln does not wear gloves."

In April of the following year, Gottschalk was on board the *Constitution* sailing toward San Francisco when he received the sad news of Lincoln's assassination. He paid his last respects by playing "The Union" while Lincoln was laid to rest over three thousand miles away.

By then, Gottschalk had traveled eighty thousand miles in two years and had given a thousand concerts, an average of three concerts every two days. Of his travels he wrote, "Eighteen hours a day on the railroad! Arrive at seven o'clock in the evening, eat with all speed, appear at eight o'clock before the public. The last note finished, rush quickly for my luggage, and en route until next day, always to the same thing! . . . The sight of a piano sets my hair on end . . . a few weeks more in this way and I would have become an idiot!"

All of Gottschalk's concerts were very popular in San Francisco, but he had a little problem with one of them. He had arranged a work for fourteen pianos, but on the eve of the event one of the pianists became ill. Gottschalk searched the city for a replacement, but could find only an amateur. Despite the young man's great confidence, he played so poorly during rehearsal that Gottschalk was certin he would ruin the performance. The composer would not consider canceling, and if he delivered only thirteen pianos when fourteen had been promised, the public would certainly feel cheated. Gottschalk solved the problem by having his tuner secretly remove the action of the amateur's piano, allowing the young man to pound away on a silent keyboard. After the performance, when Gottschalk congratulated all the pianists, the amateur complained, "The mischief! My piano broke down all at once."

Gottschalk spent three weeks playing concerts nearly every day in San Francisco, Oakland, and San Jose. He left his big Chickering grand pianos behind and traveled by stagecoach to the mining towns throughout California and the Nevada territory. The twenty-hour ride between Placerville and Carson City left him ill for three days. On another stagecoach ride on the way to Dayton, Nevada, Gottschalk felt he would be more comfortable sitting up with the driver. Though the stagecoach was quite full, the driver kept stopping along the way for more passengers. Gottschalk was shocked when a fat man hoisted himself onto the hood and rested his boots upon his shoulder. As if that were not bad enough, another man boarded the top of the stage and rested his boots on Gottschalk's other shoulder. The composer sat in angry silence, a footstool for four big dirty boots.

In Dayton, Gottschalk was embarrassed that drummers and bell ringers accompanied him on his walk from his hotel room to the theater, clanging and thumping "to call the crowd." The theater was lit by three smoking lamps and was so dark that Gottschalk could barely see the keys. The audience consisted of a few women and boys and the miners, who were dressed in flannel shirts and large grey felt hats with broad rims. "They listened attentively," Gottschalk wrote. "Their decent and tranquil manner would cause shame to many audiences that pretend to the refinement of civilization."

Gottschalk found the booming Virginia City to be "the most wearisome, the most inhospitable place on the globe," but he thought Grass Valley was charming. "Here the roses climb to the roof tops, the trees are gigantic, the brooks gayly roll their crystal waters . . . the streets are planked . . . the hotel is excellent."

For his concerts in the mining country, Gottschalk kept his music as simple as possible, careful not to "give beefsteaks to a newly born infant." He was well-received by most who heard him, though he did hear one miner complain that he had been "taken in."

After his tour through "the interior," Gottschalk returned to San Francisco to enjoy an even greater success than his previous series of concerts. His friends in San Francisco presented him with a gold medal with his initials set in diamonds on one side and the seal of California surrounded by a circle of diamonds on the reverse side. A great festival was given in Gottschalk's honor.

A few days later, however, disgrace followed on the heels of glory. Gottschalk and a representative of the Chickering Company took a carriage drive with two young ladies from the Oakland Female Seminary and returned them to the college at a late hour. Apparently a version of the story was given to the local newspaper by one of Gottschalk's enemies, because on the next day the headlines read: "VILLAINS WHO SHOULD SUFFER DEATH." The article went on to report that "a certain vagabond musician, together with a confederate" had disgraced two young women and should therefore be tarred and feathered and horsewhipped.

Like a wanted criminal, Gottschalk secretly boarded the *Colorado* and sailed to South America. The slanderous account spread throughout the country, but Gottschalk's friends came to his defense. They begged Gottschalk to defend himself, but he said he refused to dignify the slanderers with a reply. Instead, he spent the next four years in South America. Strakosch clamored for his return to the United States and founders of the National Conservatory of Music in New York invited him to be the director, but Gottschalk was not eager to return to his homeland. The pain of the scandal never left him.

In Peru, Gottschalk stumbled into the middle of a Revolutionary War and witnessed the deaths of many innocent bystanders. He traveled on to Chile, Argentina, Uruguay, and Brazil, and was successful wherever he played. Again his concert schedule left him exhausted. He contracted yellow fever but wouldn't rest long enough to completely recover.

In Rio de Janiero, Gottschalk went back into the monster-concert business. The emperor of Brazil placed at his disposal the bands of the Army, Navy, and National Guard, a total of 650 performers. Gottschalk rehearsed frantically for an entire month. He and eleven copyists worked around the clock to produce fifteen thousand pages of music—work that could have been avoided if he had only saved scores from previous festivals. The huge concert took place on November 24, 1869, in an oversold theater. The concert was a smashing success and Gottschalk announced that it would be repeated on November 26 with a reduction in the price of tickets. Only by holding the concert a second time could he hope to gain any profit, even though the military musicians were not paid.

On November 25, Gottschalk was to participate in a concert given by the Philharmonic Society. He was extremely ill and weak, but believed "the show must go on." That evening while playing his composition *Morte* (which means "she is dead"), Gottschalk fainted. Friends carried him off the stage and back to his hotel room. The next day he was hardly able to rise from his bed, but was determined to repeat the festival. Great crowds poured into the theater, but they never saw Gottschalk, who was backstage, doubled over in pain.

A friend of Gottschalk's, Dr. Severiano Martins, who had helped him recover from yellow fever in August, tried to save him again. Dr. Martins stayed with Gottschalk day and night, but could do little to help him. Louis Moreau Gottschalk died December 18, 1869. He was only forty years old.

For a while it seemed like Gottschalk's music died with him. However, in the 1930s and 1940s musicians began playing it again. Of his three hundred compositions, however, only a few dozen piano compositions are still being published today. Some people criticize Gottschalk's music for being too simple. He could write pretty melodies and interesting accompaniments but did not seem capable of developing his ideas. He wrote one square eight-measure phrase after another with little variety. Since he was not a master of form, there is much repetition in many of his works.

On the positive side, Gottschalk had a great understanding of the piano and knew how to show it off. His compositions are very "pianistic," while some composers' works for the piano are awkward to play. Almost all of Gottschalk's works are virtuosic, meaning that a pianist must be very advanced to play them. The Creole rhythms he used were innovative and foreshadowed ragtime. It is interesting to note that Gottschalk and jazz shared the same birth place—New Orleans—although Gottschalk appeared on the music scene fifty years earlier than jazz. Maybe the most appealing thing about Gottschalk's music is its spirit. It is generally happy music, lively yet elegant, and brashly American.

Perhaps if Gottschalk had lived longer his style would

have matured and he would have produced greater things. One wonders the same thing about many great composers who died young—Mozart, Schubert, and Chopin to name only a few. Gottschalk always dreamed of being rich so that he wouldn't have to perform so much and could compose more and enjoy life. Yet he gave away too much to ever have the hope of being rich. He was generous in the support of his sisters, provided a pension for his ex-slave nurse, Sally, and gave benefit concerts for many causes: the poor in Spain, the wounded soldiers of the United States Civil War, and the Society for Popular Education in Peru. This last cause was one of his favorites, for he believed that democracy was only possible if all citizens were educated.

Gottschalk was our first nationalistic composer. He took the sounds of his corner of America, shaped them into concert music, then presented them to the kings and queens of Europe. And he didn't stop there. Gottschalk was also America's first concert pianist. He believed music belonged to all people, regardless of nationality, race, wealth, or occupation. He made concert music popular in our country, taking it from big, bustling New York to the dingy mining camps of the western frontier and everywhere in between.

Edward MacDowell
Library of Congress

Chapter Two
EDWARD MACDOWELL
(1861–1908)

Thomas MacDowell was a businessman who wished that he was an artist. The sketches he drew when he was a boy proved that he was very talented. His father, however, was a devout Quaker who thought art, music, and dancing were all "stuff and nonsense." Thomas went into business to please his stern father, but he always regretted it. That is probably why Thomas encouraged his second son Edward, who showed an interest in both music and art, to use his talents.

Edward was born December 18, 1861, in the Mac-Dowell home on 220 Clinton Street in New York City. Although his father was also born in New York City, their ancestors were Celtic, both Scottish and Irish.

Edward's mother Frances was an American of English ancestry. His brother Walter was three years older than he, and his younger brother Nevin would become an artist who was well-known during his lifetime.

Although Frances was not a Quaker, the MacDowell family attended Quaker meetings on Sundays. The Quakers sat on hard benches, the women on one side of the church and the men on the other. There was no sermon or singing. People stood up and spoke "when the Spirit moved them," which wasn't very often. Edward hated sitting still for so long. When he grew up and attended any kind of church, he always stood close to the door out of fear of being trapped in a pew and unable to leave when he wanted to.

Luckily for Edward and Walter, Thomas was not as strict as his own father. On some Sundays the Mac-Dowell family piled into their horse-drawn carriage and rode three miles up Fifth Avenue to the newly opened Central Park. The park had big rocks and trees to climb and wide open spaces for running. It was as close to the country as a city boy could get. New York had no skyscrapers then, and the streets were not paved. Soldiers in blue uniforms had been guarding the city ever since the Civil War had started the year Edward was born. One of the first songs Frances taught three-year-old Edward was a popular army tune called "Tramp, Tramp, Tramp."

At age eight, Edward began taking piano lessons. His teacher was a family friend from Columbia, Juan Buitrago. Mr. Buitrago was very enthusiastic during Edward's lessons. He would talk loudly and wave his arms wildly. Edward's grandfather thought this behavior was shocking. Besides that, he thought music lessons were a waste of money. But that didn't bother Edward's parents, especially his mother. She was determined that Edward would have a musical education—no matter what her father-in-law thought.

Unfortunately, Mr. Buitrago was a violinist and didn't know much about the piano. Besides that, Edward was certainly no prodigy and he didn't like to practice. Even when he did sit down at the piano, he spent the time making up little tunes rather than practicing his assigned lesson. Once when Mr. Buitrago got carried away with a long explanation, he suddenly noticed that Edward was not paying the least bit of attention. The boy was busy sketching pictures in the margins of his music book.

Edward was actually a very good artist. At fourteen he drew a picture of himself that was very realistic, except for the mustache he added. (He wouldn't have one of those until later in life.) Edward also liked to read fairy tales. He believed in leprechauns—tiny people of Irish folklore that had to reveal the hiding place of a pot of gold if they were ever caught. Edward made up his own fairy tales and wrote down some of them.

Mr. Buitrago had a very important friend, Teresa Carreño. Miss Carreño was a famous Venezuelan concert pianist who had been a child prodigy. She was very interested in Edward's progress and occasionally gave him lessons. At first, when Edward played very well for her, she would hug and kiss him. However, she soon learned that Edward hated to be kissed. After that, she threatened to kiss him if he didn't practice diligently.

After studying several years with Mr. Buitrago, Edward began to take lessons from Paul Desvernine, a pianist who could teach him much more. Mrs. Mac-Dowell was very ambitious for Edward. She decided that he was destined to become a concert pianist. She made him practice the piano even when he would much rather have played baseball with Walter and the other boys he heard out the window.

To inspire Edward, his mother took him on a trip to Europe to visit the great musical centers of the world. Crossing the Atlantic was a big adventure for a twelve-year-old boy. For days and days, Edward saw nothing but great gray waves. He was more impressed with the ocean than any of the foreign lands he saw. Later in his life, he wrote many pieces and songs about the sea.

Edward enjoyed much of his trip to Europe. However, he supposedly had one embarrassing moment that he never forgot. Like most children, Edward loved candy. In Paris, he learned how wonderful French confectionery tasted. One day he went out alone, looking for a candy store. He walked a long time before he saw a sign that read "Confections." He didn't see any candy in the window of the shop, but then all French stores looked much different than American ones. He went in and asked for confections in his best schoolboy French. The sales girl began to giggle. She went into the back of the store and returned with a selection of frilly ladies' underwear. Edward dashed out of the store, his face redder than any of the panties he had seen.

After his European vacation, Edward returned home to take lessons from Mr. Desvernine for three more years. In April 1876, he and his mother returned to France, hoping that he would be accepted at the Paris Conservatory. Edward passed the entrance examination with flying colors. He began to attend classes in piano and theory. There he met Claude Debussy, a young nonconformist who would soon stun the musical world with his unique impressionistic compositions.

Edward had difficulty understanding his teachers who, of course, all spoke French, so Mrs. MacDowell enrolled him in a French class. Edward was so bored with the class that he constantly drew in a sketchbook hidden behind his French textbook. One afternoon he was so busy drawing his teacher's exceptionally long nose that he forgot to occasionally look up and act interested. Suddenly the teacher was beside Edward's desk with his hand extended. The boy had no choice but to show him the drawing. He was certain he would be punished because he had drawn the teacher's nose just as big as it actually was.

The teacher looked at the drawing for a long time. Finally he asked Edward where he had studied art. When the boy replied that he had never had any instruction, the teacher asked if he could keep the drawing. Edward was relieved. It didn't look like he was going to be punished after all. He gave his teacher the sketch, then promptly forgot all about it. A few days later, the teacher paid a visit to Mrs. MacDowell. Again Edward expected the worst and again he was surprised. The teacher said that he had shown Edward's drawing to a very famous painter. The artist was so impressed that he offered to give Edward free art lessons for three years and support him during his study.

Mrs. MacDowell didn't know what to say. She thanked the French teacher and told him she would consider the offer. Edward's music education was costing the family a lot of money. Having a famous artist in the family would be just as good as having a musician. Still, Mrs. MacDowell wanted Edward to be happy, so she asked him what he wanted to do. Edward thought for a long time. Up until then, he had just had fun with his art and had worked very hard at his music. He realized that music meant much more to him. "Mother, I am a musician," he said. Perhaps at that moment the art world lost a great painter; however, the music world gained a great composer.

Edward studied at the Paris Conservatory for two years before he attended a concert that would change his life. The pianist he heard was Nicholas Rubinstein. The Russian pounced on the keys with the power of his whole body. His fingers flashed like lightning. His tone was as warm as a human voice. Edward was spellbound. He had never heard anyone play the piano like that.

As he and his mother left the concert hall that summer evening, Edward thought about his study at the Paris Conservatory. He had learned to writes notes very rapidly. He had transposed nearly all the preludes and fugues of J.S. Bach. He had memorized all the rules of music theory. These exercises were good practice, but also a lot of busy work. Edward had always had a hunch that there was a lot more to music than what he was doing at the Conservatory. After hearing Rubinstein perform, he was certain of it. He turned to his mother and said, "I never can learn to play like that if I stay here."

As always, Mrs. MacDowell trusted Edward's judgment and allowed him to leave the Paris Conservatory. Together they considered many important music schools before deciding on the Stuttgart Conservatory in Germany. But Edward was also disappointed there. The German approach to music study was so different from the French that Edward soon realized he would have to start all over, and he was not willing to do that. Besides, he didn't think Stuttgart offered him as good an education as he had already received in Paris.

Edward had no idea what step to take next. Mrs. MacDowell wrote a friend for advice. The friend recommended the Frankfurt Conservatory, also in Germany. Mrs. MacDowell returned to America and Edward entered the Frankfort Conservatory in the autumn of 1879. Edward began to study piano with Carl Heymann and composition with Joachim Raff.

Heymann allowed Edward to skip tedious technical exercises and practice whatever pieces he wanted to learn. Heymann was such a dynamic pianist that Edward said of him, ". . . in hearing him practice and play I learned more in a week than I ever had before."

At first, Raff was not impressed with Edward's compositions. Edward's professors in Paris had taught him to mimic the works of great composers who had come before him. Raff urged Edward to write something "real." Edward took up this challenge by composing a work for piano entitled *First Modern Suite.*

Edward's ability as a pianist improved rapidly. When Heymann was forced to leave the conservatory due to a mental disorder two years later, he suggested that Edward teach in his place. Raff was also in favor of this. However, some of the older faculty members were opposed. They thought Edward was a brash young American who took too many liberties with the music when he played. Consequently, he was not hired for the teaching position.

Instead, Edward began to teach privately. One of his pupils was an American, Miss Marian Nevins. Edward wasn't enthused about teaching an American girl because he didn't expect her to be a serious student. Marian, on the other hand, didn't travel all the way to Germany only to study with one of her own countrymen. Nevertheless, they decided to try each other out. Edward was very strict with Marian, giving her only Bach and technical exercises for an entire year. Yet, when she had a chance to study with the famous pianist, Clara Schumann, she turned it down so that she could continue to study with Edward.

In 1881, MacDowell became head piano teacher at the Conservatory of Darmstadt. He continued to live in Frankfurt and commuted by train each day. Mac-Dowell spent forty hours a week teaching students who showed little talent. He also made a three-hour train ride to tutor some aristocratic children who lived in a real castle, complete with moat and drawbridge. Mac-Dowell could never remember the long titles of the little counts and countesses. He addressed them all improperly as "monsieur" and "mademoiselle," which didn't score any points with their mother. Once, when MacDowell was in the middle of a lecture, he was interrupted by a faint sound like the sawing of logs. His pupils were fast asleep.

It is no wonder that MacDowell considered his teaching to be drudgery. The only opportunity he had to compose was during the twelve hours of weekly railway travel. He used the time to complete his *Second Modern Suite* for piano.

Within a year, MacDowell's health began to fail. He resigned at Darmstadt and only taught privately in Frankfurt. He appeared as a pianist at orchestral concerts in Wiesbaden, Frankfurt, and Darmstadt. This gave him more prestige, but made him very little money.

One day MacDowell was fiddling around on the piano with some new ideas when someone knocked on his door. When he answered, he was amazed to find his composition teacher, Joachim Raff. The old master, who had never honored MacDowell with a visit to his home, asked his pupil what he was working on. MacDowell was so surprised by Raff's sudden appearance and the unexpected question that he lied and said he was writing a piano concerto. Raff told him to bring the new work to his lesson the following Sunday.

MacDowell had no idea how he could complete such a task, yet he wasn't willing to admit to his teacher that he lied. He had a few musical ideas jotted down that he had planned to use in a concerto at some later time. He used this material to get started, then wrote day and night. By Sunday he had only one movement completed. He sent some lame excuse to Raff and asked for his lesson to be postponed for a week. Fortunately, Raff put it off two more days. MacDowell was able to complete his concerto before the lesson.

Raff was so impressed with the concerto that he urged MacDowell to show it to Franz Liszt. By then, Liszt was an old man, regarded as one of the most important composers of the nineteenth century, and he had a reputation for helping young composers get started in the music world.

It took MacDowell a while to get up the nerve to go visit Liszt. When he finally made the journey to Weimar, he sat outside the composer's door for some time. When he got up enough courage to knock, Liszt received him warmly. MacDowell played the solo part of his concerto while a pupil of Liszt's played the orchestra part on a second piano. MacDowell was so nervous that he felt he didn't perform well. Yet when he finished, Liszt not only praised his composition, but his piano playing, too.

MacDowell left some of his other compositions with Liszt and returned to Frankfurt very encouraged. Soon after, Liszt wrote to MacDowell inviting him to play his *First Modern Suite* in the General Society of German Musicians concert series. This was MacDowell's greatest opportunity yet.

One week before the big event was to take place, Joachim Raff suddenly died. MacDowell grieved the loss of his dedicated teacher. Years later he wrote, "I had acquired from early boyhood the idea that it was expected of me to become a pianist, and every moment spent in 'scribbling' seemed to be stolen from the more legitimate work of piano practice." It was Raff who opened MacDowell's eyes to the fact that he could become a great composer. "Your music will be played when mine is forgotten," Raff once told him.

MacDowell sought consolation from his student, Marian Nevins. She encouraged him to pull himself together so that he could play well at the concert and assured him that that would be Raff's wish.

MacDowell was a smashing success. After the concert an observer asked him why he had played with the music in front of him when he had never looked at it. MacDowell then realized that he didn't think his compositions were worth studying and consciously memorizing. "I would not have changed a note in one of them for untold gold," he wrote, "and inside I had the greatest love for them; but the idea that anyone else might take them seriously had never occurred to me."

A year later, at Liszt's recommendation, both of the piano suites were published in Leipzig by the famous music publishers Breitkopf and Hartel. In gratitude, MacDowell promptly dedicated his first concerto to Liszt.

In June, 1884, MacDowell returned to America. On July 21 he married Marian Nevins at Waterford, Connecticut. The newlyweds set sail for Europe without any definite plans. During the next several years, the MacDowells traveled around Europe, finally settling in Frankfurt. MacDowell spent most of his time composing. He knew, however, that he could not expect to make a living from composition alone. He applied for teaching positions at conservatories when he heard of openings. He was rejected each time because of his youth, nationality, and "modern tendencies."

In the winter of 1886, Breitkopf and Hartel published MacDowell's first piano concerto at the same time he completed his second. That spring Marian became seriously ill, and for a time it seemed that she might die. She recovered, but lost the hope of ever bearing children.

The following year, the MacDowells purchased a little run-down cottage at the edge of the woods near Wiesbaden. They were very happy in this setting. Edward wrote a large orchestral work and many songs and piano pieces. Meanwhile, his published works were being performed around the world. Teresa Carreño, the teacher from his boyhood who threatened him with kisses, played his *Second Modern Suite* in New York.

MacDowell was pleased with his accomplishments. His only problem was that he still didn't make enough money. Many of his American friends urged him to return to his own country. At last, he and Marian decided they could make a better living in the United States. With regret, they sold their cottage and moved to Boston.

MacDowell spent the next eight years composing, teaching privately, and performing his piano works. He wrote two orchestral works and many songs and piano pieces. Perhaps the most important of these is two sonatas and *Woodland Sketches* for piano, and Suite No. 2, Op. 48 for orchestra.

The suite was nicknamed "Indian" because MacDowell based the themes on authentic North American Indian music. A solemn three-note theme opens the piece and is heard in all five movements. This theme represents the great past of a dying race. The first movement, entitled "Legend," includes music of the Iroquois and Chippewa. For "Love Song," MacDowell borrowed music from the Iowas. The material in "In War-time" is closely related to the Iroquois scalp dance. "Dirge," a funeral march, is based on a Kiowa woman's lament and ends with the plaintive call of a trumpet played off-stage. "Dirge" is included in the handful of pieces that MacDowell thought were his very best. The final movement, "Village Festival," is a rapid, rollicking dance that opens with lively pizzicato violins meaning that the strings are plucked. It ends with solemn majesty—MacDowell's final tribute to "the vanishing American."

Though MacDowell borrowed music from Native Americans, he denied that he was a nationalistic composer. Many people would argue that MacDowell's music sounds more Celtic than American. His style is similar to that of the Norwegian composer Edvard Grieg, whom MacDowell admired so much that he dedicated his third and fourth piano sonatas to him. However, MacDowell did not believe there is such a thing as nationalistic music. He didn't think music can be confined in the boundaries that divide nations. He once proved his point by showing how similar Native

American music was to Russian folk songs. MacDowell
insisted that it is the unique personality of an individual, not his nationality, that causes one composer's
music to be different from another's.

The Boston years were happy ones for MacDowell.
One of his greatest triumphs there was when the
Boston Symphony played his *Indian Suite* and "Second
Concerto" on the same program, with MacDowell
himself appearing as the solo pianist. MacDowell made
many friends in Boston and greatly enjoyed their company. However, he was a shy person and was uncomfortable in large gatherings of mere acquaintances and
strangers. He had two dogs, a collie named Charle-
magne and, later, a terrier named Charlie. MacDowell
taught Charlie to be a music critic. He barked happily
when he heard the music of Wagner and howled when
he heard Brahms.

In 1896, MacDowell was invited to create a music
department in the new Columbia University in his
hometown, New York City. He was reluctant to give
up the independence he enjoyed in Boston but the
position offered a guaranteed income and an opportunity to influence young American musicians. MacDowell accepted the offer, a decision that proved to be a
mistake.

MacDowell's work load at Columbia University was
tremendous. He single-handedly taught five separate
courses of study: general music, history, theory, counterpoint, and composition. Today, so many subjects
would be taught by several faculty members. During
the second year, one of MacDowell's best pupils, Leon-

ard McWhood, was hired to assist him. But MacDowell still taught five courses that year and six the following year. Besides lecturing, he spent tedious hours correcting exercises and exams. He also devoted Sunday mornings to private instruction for advanced students in piano and composition.

MacDowell enjoyed his few talented students, but he was impatient with the dull ones. Still, he kept his sense of humor. Once when a student completed an exercise with several measures of rests, the musical symbol for silence, MacDowell marked the section with a red pencil and wrote, "This is the only correct passage in the exercise!"

MacDowell was not suited for such a structured job and was often exhausted. During his eight years at Columbia he had no time to practice the piano. Fortunately he was a natural pianist and didn't need to work very hard to play well. The critics praised his performances, but he was not at all satisfied. In fact, MacDowell had so little confidence during this time that sometimes his wife had to shove him onto the stage to get him started. He was able to give only a few concerts, except during his sabbatical leave beginning in 1902. For two years he toured across the country all the way to San Francisco.

MacDowell had little time to compose during the school year, but he disciplined himself to write a few measures every day, no matter how busy he was. This did not result in complete pieces, but rather in mere sketches of musical ideas. He did most of his composing in the summer on his farm near Peterboro, New Hampshire. There, MacDowell took out the sketches he had made during the school year and worked them into finished pieces and songs.

MacDowell had purchased the Peterboro property in 1896. It consisted of a small farmhouse, fifteen acres of farm land, and fifty acres of woods. In these woods, MacDowell built a small log cabin with a spacious fireplace. He furnished it with a couch, table, and two chairs.

Among the many works MacDowell composed at Peterboro are three collections of piano pieces, *Sea Pieces, Fireside Tales*, and *New England Idyls*. Many of these pieces and those in *Woodland Sketches*, are not more than a page or two long. MacDowell is sometimes called a miniaturist because many of his best works are so short. If you have taken piano lessons for four years or more, you might ask your teacher if you can play some of the pieces in these collections.

MacDowell was a visual composer. He would often imagine a beautiful scene that inspired him to paint a musical picture. His love of nature is reflected in many of his titles: "To the Sea," "The Joy of Autumn," "Told At Sunset," and his most famous, "To A Wild Rose." Sometimes MacDowell also wrote a few words or short poem about the scene. For his piece "In Deep Woods" he wrote:

> *Above, long slender shafts of opal flame,*
> *Below, the dim cathedral aisles;*
> *The silent mystery of immortal things*
> *Broods o'er the woods at eve.*

Music that depicts a scene or tells a story is called program music. Music that does not, like most symphonies and sonatas, is called absolute music. Most composers write either one or the other. Although MacDowell wrote program music, he felt that the imagery was secondary to the music. Picturing certain scenes in his mind helped him get his music down on paper, but he didn't think listeners had to imagine the same scene in order to appreciate his music.

MacDowell also wrote a lot of songs in his log cabin. In fact, his forty-two songs make up one-third of his entire output. He was very particular about what words he set to music. He read and admired a lot of poetry, but he didn't think that much of it was easy to sing. He once rejected an entire poem simply because it contained "nostrils," a word he didn't think was singable. As a result, MacDowell wrote a lot of his own lyrics. He was so modest, however, that he didn't attach his name to the words when the songs were published.

Aside from the two suites mentioned earlier, MacDowell wrote very little for orchestra. He once explained that it was difficult to get orchestral works performed, whereas whenever he wanted to hear his piano pieces and songs, all he had to do was sit down at the piano.

When Edward was not composing in Peterboro, he enjoyed gardening, photography, horseback riding, and hunting. Marian called this latter hobby "pretending to hunt" because he was so in love with nature that he had no real desire to kill any living thing. Edward also

loved literature, especially Mark Twain, Tennyson, and
Joel Chandler Harris's "Uncle Remus" stories, and he
frequently read aloud to Marian in the evenings. He
enjoyed a good game of golf and donated some of his
land for a public course so that his neighbors, both
rich and poor, could play.

When MacDowell returned to Columbia in the autumn of 1903 after his sabbatical, he found that a lot
had changed in his absence. A new president, Nicholas
Murray Butler, had taken over as head of the university. Butler had ideas that were quite different from
MacDowell's. He did a lot of reorganizing without
asking MacDowell's opinion, which upset MacDowell
and made him very nervous. This, along with the
strain of work, caused his health to fail. After much
discussion with his wife during the Christmas holiday,
MacDowell decided to quietly resign at the end of the
school year.

News of MacDowell's resignation leaked out early.
One afternoon in February, two cub reporters came to
visit him. At first the composer would not say anything
to them. But when one of them accused him of being
a quitter, MacDowell blurted out all his frustrations in
a stream of anger. He said that all his rash comments
were "off the record" and begged the reporters not to
publish them. Of course the young reporters weren't
going to let such a big scoop slip by them. The next
day, the whole story was published in the *New York
Times*.

MacDowell and President Butler fired away at each
other, both privately and in further newspaper articles.

Butler accused MacDowell of making his assistant, McWhood, do all the work. Angry and hurt, MacDowell sent Butler a schedule showing how many classes he and McWhood each taught. When McWhood was later hired to fill MacDowell's position, the composer unjustly accused McWhood of being disloyal. MacDowell was so upset he couldn't think straight.

Today, the matter is almost completely forgotten. Columbia University is proud of the fact that MacDowell was its first professor of music. But MacDowell couldn't forget. His pride and feelings were crushed. He was not able to just shrug his shoulders and turn to his composing. Instead, he brooded and brooded. One day he was so deep in thought that he crossed the street right in front of a taxi cab and was hit and seriously injured.

Perhaps if MacDowell had completely rested for a year or so he could have avoided his tragic end. Instead, he continued to teach privately. In the spring of 1905, after only a year of teaching, his mind simply stopped working. At both his home in Westminster Hotel in New York City and at Peterboro, MacDowell sat quietly, staring vacantly. Occasionally he turned the pages of a book of fairy tales or smiled in recognition at his wife and close friends.

No one is quite sure what happened to MacDowell. Perhaps he had a nervous breakdown or a brain tumor. Perhaps his premature senility was actually Alzheimer's disease, a disorder that little is known about even today.

MacDowell died quietly at the Westminster Hotel on

January 23, 1908, with his beloved Marian at his side. He was buried at Peterboro on a hilltop overlooking one of his favorite views. On a bronze tablet attached to a large boulder are the words he wrote to accompany his piano piece, "From a Log Cabin":

> A *house of dreams untold,*
> *It looks out over the whispering tree-tops*
> *And faces the setting sun.*

MacDowell had been very productive in his log cabin. He once remarked to his wife that he wished other composers and artists had the opportunity to spend time producing works at his retreat. Marian remembered Edward's wish after he died. She spent the rest of her life playing concert tours of his piano pieces. With the money she earned, she built many more log cabins in the woods at Peterboro. Today it is the site of the MacDowell Artists Colony. Composers, artists, and writers go there to work in peace, without interruption from the outside world.

Some people think Edward MacDowell was overly sentimental and old-fashioned. While his harmony may not have been unusual, he was able to use old ideas in a free new way. His works sound the way only one man, Edward MacDowell, could write music. He had a great gift of melody and his songs are some of his best works. His music is not psychologically complex, yet it is filled with emotion. His works reflect tenderness, joy, longing, power, love, and, especially, the simple pleasures of nature. MacDowell has been called "A Listener to the Winds"—he wrote in his music what he heard the winds say.

Charles Ives in Battery Park, New York City 1913
From the Charles Ives Papers in the Music Library of Yale University

Chapter Three
CHARLES IVES
(1874-1954)

When Charles Ives was a boy, his father stretched his ears. That doesn't mean his father pulled the lobes or yanked the tops. It means that George Ives taught his son how to listen to the whole world of sound.

During one thunderstorm, Charlie watched his father run back and forth between the backyard and the piano in the parlor. The church bells next door were clanging and clattering and George was trying to find all the bell tones on the piano. He discovered that he couldn't find the exact combination because piano keys are a half step apart and the bells were sounding quarter tones, pitches that exist in between the keys. Not long afterward, George built a machine that would play the tones "in the cracks between the piano keys."

George also had Charlie sing a tune like "Swanee River" in the key of E flat while he played the accompaniment in the key of C. The melody in one key clashed with the chords in the other key. Playing in two keys at once was later named bitonality. It didn't have a name when George was using it because the idea was so new.

When Charlie took up the drums, the neighbors complained about his noisy practicing. He then played his drumming exercises on the piano. Charlie's father encouraged him to play with his fist or the flat of his hand. The great clumps of keys he mashed down were later named tone clusters.

Charlie's father taught him another valuable ear-stretching exercise. Once a young musician complained to George about an old man's singing in church. The musician asked, "How can you stand to hear old John Bell bellow off-key?" George replied, "Look into his face and hear the music of the ages. Don't pay too much attention to the sounds. If you do, you may miss the music. You won't get a wild, heroic ride to heaven on pretty little sounds." To George, the way music *feels* was more important than the way it *sounds*.

George kept all these ear-stretching exercises very private because he didn't think the general public would understand. The Iveses were highly respected in their town of Danbury, Connecticut. Charlie's great-grandfather Isaac operated such a successful hat factory that Danbury became known as "hat town." Isaac also owned the first bathroom in Fairfield County, which people came from miles around to see.

Charlie's grandfather George took over the hat business and made it even more profitable. He started the first bank in Danbury from a wooden chest in his dining room. When the bank grew, he moved it to a desk and then to a building next door. The first three of his five children also became wealthy. His youngest son was a musician and the "black sheep" of the family. He was Charlie's father, George.

When George was seventeen he led a volunteer band in the Civil War. General Ulysses S. Grant supposedly told Abraham Lincoln that it was the best band in the Union Army. However, Grant was not much of a music critic. He once claimed that he recognized two tunes: "One is 'Yankee Doodle'; the other one isn't."

George returned from the war and became the bandmaster of Danbury. His family thought that that was "just kind of foolishness." Music was supposed to be entertainment, not an occupation. In 1874, George married Mary Elizabeth Parmelee, whom everyone called Mollie. She was a woman of simple tastes and had little education. George and Molly had two sons, Charles Edward, born October 20, 1874, and Joseph Moss, born two years later. George was sometimes forced to take odd jobs and later worked as a clerk in his father's bank. His mother had her barn converted into a house for George's family. The rest of the Iveses thought of him as a "poor relation."

When Charlie was five, George started teaching him

Charles Ives at 14, already a composer of orchestral music and the youngest organist in Connecticut to receive a paycheck
From the Charles Ives Papers in the Music Library of Yale University

music theory and music history. George taught Charlie to play the piano, cornet, and violin. Charlie also played the drums in his father's band. He heard and played classical music, popular tunes, band marches, hymns in church, and fiddling at barn dances.

Charles began composing at age thirteen. His first orchestra piece, *Holiday Quickstep*, was performed by his father's theater orchestra in January of 1888. At age fourteen he became the organist for the New Baptist Church in Danbury. He was the youngest organist in the state to receive a paycheck. The next year he began taking organ lessons from a well-known organist, Alexander Gibson. Throughout his teens, Charles composed organ and choir music that he could play on the job. He also composed marches for the Danbury band.

In February of 1893, Charles moved to New Haven to attend the Hopkins Grammar School, where he studied for the entrance exams to Yale University. Charlie loved sports, especially baseball. During grammar school he was captain of a team called "The Alerts." Later in life he wrote a piano piece called *Some Southpaw Pitching*. During his first year in New Haven, Charles played the organ at St. Thomas Church. The following year, he became the organist at

Charles (seated on the bench, far left) and his baseball team, "The Alerts"
From the Charles Ives Papers in the Music Library of Yale University

Center Church in New Haven and remained at that post for four years. This was a very important position—the organ instructor at Yale had held it before Charles.

A young woman named Harmony Twitchell often attended services at Center Church. Some Yale men called her "the most beautiful girl in Hartford." At first Harmony thought the way the organist harmonized hymns was a little strange, but she grew to like it. Later, when Charles attended Yale, Harmony's brother David introduced him to his sister. Years later, Harmony and Charles met again and began dating.

Charles entered Yale in September 1894 at the age of twenty. Two months later his father unexpectedly died, leaving a big empty place in Charles's life. He hoped that Horatio Parker, his music teacher at Yale, could partly fill it.

Parker, however, wasn't at all sympathetic toward Charles or his music. He was very proud of his German musical training. To him, American culture was backward and crude compared to the refined European tradition. He saw Ives as a mediocre talent who had been trained by a country bumpkin of a bandmaster. He started Charles from scratch, assigning him exercises in the same music theory book that he had used as a child.

Still Charles didn't forget what his father had taught him. He included quarter tones, bitonality, and tone clusters in his compositions. Parker thought Ives's music was too wild to be taken seriously. Once Ives showed Parker a composition in which four different melodies were going on in four different keys all at once. Parker accused Ives of "hogging all the keys at one meal." He asked Ives not to bring any more pieces like that to class. Ives then began to compose "textbook" compositions for Parker and experimental compositions for himself.

There was no such thing as a music major when Ives was going to college. Nevertheless, he spent most of his time on music and got barely passing grades in all his other subjects. He also played baseball and football for Yale and competed on the track team. He had an active social life that was centered around his fraternity, Delta Kappa Epsilon. He often composed music for fraternity shows, including "Hells Bells: The Fight that Yaled." He also wrote the school song, "The Bells of Yale," which is still sung today. For a long time it seemed that Ives would be remembered only for this one song.

While at Yale, Ives wrote more than eighty works, including forty songs and the "First String Quartet." He was especially proud of his organ music, *Prelude and Postlude for Thanksgiving Service*. He called it "his first serious pieces away from the German rule book." Parker "made some fairly funny cracks about it." However, Dr. John Cornelius Griggs, the choir director at Center Church, liked it. He recognized Ives's talent and tried to convince Parker of it. In this way Dr. Griggs eased some of the pain Ives felt about the loss of his father.

For his senior project, Ives composed his "First Symphony." Parker asked him to make many changes in it so that it would sound more like German classical music. Ives didn't want to make any of the changes, but he did anyway. He was bitter about having to make a good piece not so good just so his teacher would give him a passing grade. Even so, Ives respected and admired Parker. The worst thing he ever said about him was that "his mind and his heart were never around together." After Ives graduated, he changed his "First Symphony" back to the way he wanted it.

After graduating from Yale, Ives was faced with a career decision. He knew he couldn't make money as a composer. He managed to get a new post as organist at Bloomfield First Presbyterian Church in New Jersey, but his salary only covered his rent. He remembered his father's struggle to make a living as a musician and didn't want that for himself. He knew that many men in his family had been successful businessmen and he thought he could be, too. A distant relative offered him a job at Mutual Life Insurance Company and he gladly accepted it. His starting salary was five dollars per week.

Ives shared an apartment with six or seven other Yale graduates who were getting their start in the business world. The young men jokingly called their home "Poverty Flat." Besides holding down his church and insurance jobs, Ives attended law school at night. He also pitched for his agency's baseball team. He spent all his other waking hours at a piano in a back room of the apartment, hammering out new compositions.

Ives's roommates kidded him about his composing. He wrote, "Three quite right critics say I haven't got the tune right and the chords are wrong . . . Keyes says these notes are O.K.—he is the best critic, for he doesn't know one note from another."

In the spring of 1900, Ives became organist at the Central Presbyterian Church in New York, just around the corner from Poverty Flat. He talked his roommates into joining the choir. One of them insisted that he didn't know anything about singing, but Ives told him it made no difference. All he had to do was "make his mouth go."

Two years later, Ives resigned from his organist position and never worked as a professional musician again. He felt the music he was composing and performing at church services was too different from what the churchgoers expected to hear. He wrote, "How far has a man a right to do what he wants, if he knows that by so doing he is interfering with the state of mind of the listeners, who have to listen regardless, and are helpless not to?"

In 1902 Charles began dating Harmony Twitchell. By then she had graduated as a registered nurse and had worked as a companion/nurse for four years. Harmony was an avid reader in three languages—French, German, and English. She and Charles shared a love for literature. She often read aloud to him. She also wrote poetry, including lyrics for some of his songs.

Ives had a mild heart attack in 1906 at the age of thirty-two, which might have caused him to worry that his life would be cut short. After that he worked more furiously than ever. He composed from midafternoon until early morning and every Saturday and Sunday.

On January 1, 1909, Ives and Julian Myrick formed a

new agency financed by Mutual Life. Ives & Myrick grew to be the largest and most prosperous agency in the insurance business.

Ives and Myrick were very different men, but they made a great team. Myrick took care of all the day-to-day business of hiring and firing the agents and managing the office. Ives did all the organizing, planning, and writing. He started the first school for insurance agents. He wrote many pamphlets to use as education materials for the new agents. His pamphlet *The Amount to Carry and How to Carry It* told the agents how to figure out how much insurance to sell each customer. The pamphlet is still in use today.

Life insurance used to be a luxury purchased only by the rich. When a man who earned only a modest income died, his wife and family usually could not make their house payments and would lose their home. Ives devised a plan so that people of lower and middle incomes could afford life insurance by paying for it a little bit each month. Ives felt it was his mission in the insurance business to protect families and their homes.

So Ives actually lived two lives. In private he was a composer and in public he was an insurance man. Composer Henry Cowell liked to tell a story about this double life. One day while Cowell was riding a bus, a man sitting next to him struck up a conversation. The man introduced himself as an estate insurance lawyer. He began to talk a long time about an amazing insurance man named Charles Ives who had invented estate insurance. Cowell showed the man part of a book that he and his wife Sidney were writing. It was about an amazing composer named Charles Ives. The estate lawyer thought he knew Ives's work very well, but he had not known that Ives also composed music.

Ives never complained that he had to earn a living in business when he would rather be composing. He once wrote:

> *The fabric of existence weaves itself whole. You can not set art off in the corner and hope for it to have vitality, reality, and substance. There can be nothing "exclusive" about a substantial art. It comes directly out of the heart of experience of life and thinking about life and living life. My work in music helped my business and my work in business helped my music.*

Ives's outlook on life was the same as the transcendentalists'. Transcendentalists think that feelings "transcend," or go beyond, thinking. For instance, an intellectual might clip a rose, dissect it in a laboratory, and study it scientifically before deciding its worth. A transcendentalist would see and smell the rose, then value it for what it made him feel.

Ives greatly admired the American transcendental authors Ralph Waldo Emerson, Henry David Thoreau, and Amos Bronson Alcott (who was Louisa May Alcott's father). The movements of Ives's most famous piano work, The *Concord* Sonata, are named "Emerson," "Hawthorne," "The Alcotts," and "Thoreau."

On June 9, 1908, Charles and Harmony were finally married. Harmony is a lovely name for a composer's wife and it suited Mrs. Ives's disposition. Her calm nature soothed Charles's nervous excitability, which in later years was so extreme that it threatened his life.

Although she was not a musician, she recognized Charles as a musical genius. In his *Memos* Ives wrote:

> One thing I am certain of is that, if I have done anything good in music, it was, first, because of my father, and second, because of my wife . . . she never once said or suggested or looked or thought that there must be something wrong with me— a thing implied, if not expressed, by most everybody else, including members of the family. She never said, "Now why don't you be good, and write something nice the way they like it?"—Never! She urged me on my way—to be myself! She gave me not only help but a confidence that no one else since father had given me.

A year after their marriage, Harmony had to have an emergency operation that left her unable to have children. Both she and Charles felt a loss, for they had hoped to have a family.

During the summer of 1915, the Iveses invited the Osbornes, a large poor family, to stay in the guest house on their farm in West Redding, Connecticut. The Osborne baby, Edith, was very sick. Her mother had a hard time taking care of her and her many other children. Harmony offered to care for the baby in their home and Mrs. Osborne gladly accepted. Gradually Harmony nursed Edith back to health. Charles and Harmony grew to love the child and found it hard to give her up. The Osbornes allowed them to adopt her.

It was good that Harmony was a nurse because Edith remained sickly and frail throughout her life. In addition, Charles suffered from heart trouble, cataracts, diabetes, and palsy. The palsy sometimes caused him to shake so badly that his handwriting was difficult to read.

On October 1, 1918, Charles suffered a major heart attack from which he never fully recovered. Three years later he all but stopped composing. No one is certain why, but his health was at least part of the reason. It seems that he wore himself out early in life. He spent his remaining thirty-three years doing what he called "cleaning house." He reworked, arranged, and copied his compositions to get them ready for publication.

Although Ives lived to be seventy-nine, he composed almost all his important works between 1900 and 1920. In twenty years he wrote an incredible amount of music, including five symphonies, two orchestral "sets" or suites, two string quartets, six violin and piano sonatas, two huge piano sonatas and other pieces for piano and organ, and over two hundred songs.

Ives used a lot of dissonance in his music meaning that the notes clashed and created tension. The people of his time, preferred consonant music that blended and made them feel relaxed. They thought dissonance was too harsh, even ugly. For this reason, Ives rarely heard his music played during the time that he composed. Most conductors weren't willing perform it because it was so difficult to learn. Ives did hold some private rehearsals and persuaded a few orchestras to perform his music, but it was often poorly done. Even when it was played well, critics gave him terrible reviews. Ives called critics who didn't like dissonance "lily boys" and "weak sisters." He called music without dissonance "lady-finger music" and "nice little easy sugar plum sounds."

In 1920, Ives paid for the publication of his *Concord Sonata*. The piece is so complicated that he thought it needed an explanation. He therefore also published *Essays Before a Sonata*. Ives waited a long time before he heard the complete *Concord* Sonata performed. Pianist John Kirkpatrick practiced it for ten years before debuting it in 1939.

In 1922, Ives published *114 Songs*, also at his own expense. He sent his songs to musicians, composers, and anyone else he thought might be interested. The volume contains a wide assortment. There are cowboy songs, hymns, songs adapted from instrumental music, humorous songs, and sad songs. Some of the songs are very simple and sweet while others are complex and dissonant. Ives even suggested that some of the songs were so complex that they could not be sung. He claimed that the songs themselves might prefer not to be sung because "A song has a few rights the same as other ordinary citizens."

"Two Little Flowers" is a short song with lyrics written by Harmony. She describes different flowers in her yard, "but fairest, rarest of them all" are Edith and her playmate, Susanna. The song sounds sentimental and sweet but Ives builds an interesting complication into the piano part. Each measure contains eight eighth notes. The accompaniment pattern, however, is based on seven. The pattern shifts over one eighth-note beat each time it starts over.

Ives borrows the lyrics and melody for "At the River"

from Robert Lowry's hymn, "Shall We Gather at the River?", though he changes pitches and rhythms to suit his own style. The piano accompaniment is taken from his own Fourth Violin Sonata. A singer performing this song must be very sure of his part because the pianist is playing something completely different most of the time. It seems like the parts don't belong together, yet they make a good team. The dissonant chords give strength to the lyrics. It is as if the singer can not be tempted away from "the river that flows by the throne of God," even though the accompaniment tries to lead him astray.

"Charlie Rutlage" is a song about a cowboy who meets his fate underneath his fallen horse. As Charlie nears his end, the singer breaks into speech, as if the tale is too exciting to merely sing. The pianist works up to such a horrible racket that by the time the horse falls, she is punching out huge tone clusters with her fists.

In his song "General Booth Enters Heaven," Ives imagines what it was like when the founder of the Salvation Army died and went to heaven. The song opens with the piano imitating the Salvation Army Band drum beat. Throughout the piece, Ives uses word painting—the music depicts the meaning of particular words. For instance, when "banjo" is mentioned in the lyrics, the voice part includes a bit of "Golden Slippers," a pop tune that was frequently accompanied by banjo. On the word "trumpet," the voice part wails out a traditional bugle call. When Booth leads his followers "round and round, round and round and round" the courthouse square in heaven, the singer sings round and round three notes and the piano plays round and round the same three notes, only in the opposite direction as the singer and in a different rhythm. At the end of the song, Ives uses traditional hymnbook harmony. It sounds very pure and holy after all the wild and woolly musical effects that come before it. The accompaniment ends with another drum beat, which grows softer and softer, as if General Booth's Salvation Army Band is marching out of sight.

Certainly Ives was thinking of his own father when he set to music the following Anne Collins poem, "The Greatest Man."

My teacher said us boys should write about some great man, so I thought last night 'n' thought about heroes and men that'd done great things, 'n' then I got to thinkin' 'bout my pa; he ain't a hero 'r anything, but pshaw! Say! he can ride the wildest hoss 'n find minners near the moss down by the creek; 'n he can swim 'n fish—we ketched five newlights, me 'n him! Dad's some hunter, too—oh, my! Miss Molly Cottontail sure does fly when he tromps through the field 'n brush! (Dad won't kill a lark 'r thrush.) Once when I was sick 'n though his hands were rough he rubbed the pain right out. "That's stuff!" he said, when I winked back the tears. He never cried but once, 'n that was when my mother died. There's lots o' great men, George Washington 'n Lee, but Dad's got 'em all beat holler, seems to me!

"The Greatest Man" is set simply in four beats per measure, but it doesn't sound that way. The meter seems irregular because Ives sets the phases according to speech patterns. Accented exclamations like "pshaw! Say!" land on unaccented beats. Other phrases that portray the boy's enthusiasm are run together so that no meter is felt. The last phrase, "seems to me!", is delayed, beginning on the weak second beat as if the boy has embarrassed himself by speaking up and suddenly hangs back.

Through the publication of The *Concord* Sonata and *114 Songs* Ives gradually became known in the musical world. Aaron Copland, a composer who received a copy of Ives's songs wrote, "How, I wondered, does a man of such gifts manage to go on creating in a vacuum with no audience at all . . . To write all that music and not hear it, one would have to have the courage of a lion."

Ives was not influenced by other modern composers because he never heard their music. Harmony once said he heard Debussy's *La Mer* and Stravinsky's *Firebird* around 1912, but that was all. Ives's influences were classical music, the popular music of his boyhood, hymns, band music, and American folk music.

Ives "quotes" this music in nearly all of his major works. While listening to Ives, you might hear a part of "Camptown Races" or a bit of "Nearer, My God to Thee," as well as the famous opening of Beethoven's "Fifth Symphony." This music stirred Ives's emotions. He wanted to transfer these feelings into his own music. He wove, blended, and mixed the music he loved with his own ideas. The resulting concoction was his own unique style.

By quoting existing music, Ives kept in the spirit of transcendentalism. The transcendentalists felt that everything was a part of everything else. It made perfect sense to Ives to toss "Yankee Doodle" into a symphony if he thought the piece needed the emotional impact of "Yankee Doodle."

Ives was never afraid of composing a "failure" like composers who wrote for the public were. He was willing to try anything. Many of his ideas, which he called "take-offs," never got off the ground.

Ives worked on one piece about a boat that was sunk by an explosion. Not only did he want the explosion to be heard, he wanted it to be visible on his music paper. He also had the idea that the "feel" of a football game could be transmitted through music if the notes on the pages moved in the kinds of formations that players use on the football field.

Ives's explosion music and football music were never completed, nor was his *Universe Symphony*. For this huge work he planned to have several orchestras and choruses positioned on hill tops, mountainsides, and valleys. This project was so big in his mind that he invited other composers to work on it, too.

Much of Ives's music reflects his patriotism. He hated war more than anything, but once the United States got involved in World War I, he was willing to support his country. In June, 1917, he asked his insurance agents to give two days of their time to sell Liberty Bonds. At his own expense, he wrote, printed, and distributed a circular urging civilians to do their part in the war effort. Ives wrote, "A pleasure car is non-essential. The allies need your gasoline. Release your chauffeur for work in the army, factory or farm . . . Let the soldiers have the smokes . . . The Soldier gives up everything. What are you giving up?"

In 1920, Ives drafted a twentieth amendment to the Constitution that would give the common man more say in the government. In it, he suggested that the voting age be lowered to eighteen and he proposed that war could be declared only through a popular vote. Ives sent an article about his twentieth amendment to the *New York Times* and other leading New York newspapers, but it was never published. He then sent the amendment to President Wilson, Governor Calvin Coolidge of Massachusetts, Herbert Hoover (then Secretary of the Navy), William Howard Taft (then a law professor at Yale), and others. The only reply he received was from Taft, who wrote, "I am very much opposed to approve such an amendment . . . It is impracticable, and would much change the form of our Government."

Taft was right, of course; war must be declared quickly, there is no time for each citizen to cast a vote. However, the episode shows Ives's trust in the democratic way. He truly believed that one United States citizen could single-handedly restructure the government by merely launching a letter-writing campaign.

Due to poor health, Ives was forced to retire from business in 1930. He divided his time between his home in New York City and his farm in West Redding. He, Harmony, and Edith made four trips to Europe in 1924, 1932, 1934, and 1938.

In 1927, Ives met composer Henry Cowell and the two became lifelong friends. Cowell did much to get

Ives's work known. Cowell published Ives's music in his quarterly *New Music* and arranged for it to be played in concerts. Ives gave Cowell money to help finance *New Music* and to produce concerts of modern music.

To perform Ives's music was a major undertaking because his scores were in a horrible state. Some were in pencil almost too light to read. Others had corrections that were patched onto other scores. Sometimes when Ives hired copyists to prepare his work for performance, they merely photocopied the score and cut and glued the different instrument parts together. The result was unreadable. Other copyists were too careful and tried to correct Ives's "mistakes." On the "Fourth of July" score, Ives wrote, "Mr. Price, Please don't try to make things nice! All the wrong notes are *right*. Just copy as I have. I want it that way."

Henry Cowell, Elliott Carter, and Lou Harrison were all composers who helped Ives get his scores in shape. Many times when they asked him about this note or that, Ives would reply, "Either way, one is as good as another." It didn't seem to make any difference to him.

In 1947, Ives received the Pulitzer Prize for his "Third Symphony." The Pulitzer is a great honor, but Ives didn't seem that impressed by it. "Awards and prizes are for school children, and I'm no longer a school boy," he said.

This is all quite puzzling. On one hand it seems like it was very important to Ives that his music become known. On the other hand, it seems like it didn't matter to him at all. Perhaps recognition came to him

The first page of the Fourth Symphony. Ives composed in pencil with a shaky hand, making his manuscripts nearly impossible to read
From the Charles Ives Papers in the Music Library of Yale University

too late in life. After all, he received the Pulitzer *forty years* after he did all the work. Perhaps his joy was in the composing and after it was all done it didn't matter to him what happened to the music.

Conductor Nicholas Slonimsky said, "Basically it made very little difference to him whether he was or was not played or recognized. He felt that he was doing the right thing, and nobody could change that conviction."

Elliott Carter wonders why Ives put up with such

terrible performances of his music. He is not so certain that it was simply because Ives didn't care. Rather, he cared so much that it could threaten his life. Carter recalls that once when Ives was playing part of his *Concord* Sonata in his own home,

> *a vein on the side of his neck began to bulge as if it were going to burst with the tremendous energy and excitement he was putting into the performance. Apparently accustomed to this, he stopped playing, pinched the vein as if to stop the flow of blood and went to lie down on a sofa to recover, his wife bringing him a glass of milk.*

The older Ives got, the more he looked backward through time. He shook his fist at airplanes flying overhead and rarely used the telephone. He didn't own a radio and he didn't play phonograph records. He didn't read newspapers—not because he didn't care what was going on, but because the miseries of the world upset him too much. He felt that the American people had changed, that they were too greedy for money. He made plenty himself, but he gave most of it away.

Though Ives's farm in West Redding was very close to Danbury, he didn't return to his hometown for fifteen or twenty years. When he finally spent one night there, he sorely regretted it. Danbury had changed with the times and Ives felt a great yearning for the way things were when he was a boy.

As a grown man, Ives frequently thought and spoke about his boyhood. His overwhelming nostalgia is best conveyed in *Holidays Symphony*, also known as *New*

England Holidays, which he composed between 1897 and 1913. He didn't call this symphony by a number like his other four because he thought of it as a suite, or what he called an "orchestral set." Each of the four movements is named for a different holiday and represents a different season: "George Washington's Birthday" in winter, "Decoration Day" in spring, "The Fourth of July" in summer, and "Thanksgiving and Forefathers' Day" in fall.

"George Washington's Birthday" opens with a slow dissonant introduction that gives the feeling of a cold, bleak February evening. A rip-roaring barn dance then erupts with snatches of "Camptown Races," "Turkey in the Straw," and "The Campbells Are Coming." The strings slip-slide through the tunes like bluegrass fiddles. Twanging out a humorous melody is a Jew's harp—an elastic strip of metal attached to a frame held in the player's teeth. The barn dance draws to a close when "Good Night, Ladies" resounds wistfully in the flute and strings.

Decoration Day, which is now called Memorial Day, is a time to pay tribute to all soldiers who have lost their lives while defending our country. When Ives was a boy, the townspeople of Danbury spent the day decorating the graves of Civil War veterans. The movement "Decoration Day" is divided into three parts that depict the townspeople gathering on the green in the town center, the procession to the cemetery, and the march home again. Fragments of hymn tunes are heard in the slow middle section. A reverent rendition of "Taps" is sounded softly and distantly by the trumpet.

The quickstep home is a comic take-off of a popular band number from Ives's boyhood called "Second Regiment Connecticut National Guard March."

Ives was especially pleased with his "Fourth of July" movement. He kept it in a safe at the Ives & Myrick insurance offices. Myrick found it in his side of the safe one day when they were moving their business to a new location. Knowing that Ives had cleaned out his portion of the safe, Myrick asked Ives if he should toss out that stack of old music papers. "My God, Mike!" Ives exclaimed. "That's the best thing I've written." Ives later dedicated the movement to Myrick.

When Ives composed this movement, he imagined a particular Fourth of July from his boyhood. Women are unloading picnic baskets, kids are shooting off firecrackers, and the men are having heated political arguments. The Danbury Band marches around the town square, blasting out "Columbia the Gem of the Ocean," with Charles's own father in the lead, his cornet glinting in the sunlight. Some of the brass players honk out a few wrong notes, others go flat, and some miss a few beats, but that doesn't matter because the spirit of the thing is there. Just then, *another* band begins tramping around the town square in the opposite direction, blaring "The Battle Hymn of the Republic" in a key that is most certainly not the one played by the hometown favorites. When the two bands, going at all out, full-lung power pass one another—well! You can just imagine the glorious, uproarious clamor of it all!

For the fourth movement, "Thanksgiving and Forefathers' Day," Ives used much of the material from *Organ Prelude and Postlude for Thanksgiving*, which he wrote while he was a student at Yale. The movement opens with clashing major and minor chords. To Ives this dissonance represented "the sternness and strength and austerity of the Puritan character." Fragments of hymn tunes are heard faintly in the woodwinds and violins like the way a choir singing inside a church would sound to someone standing outside in the churchyard.

Though most of the movement is very solemn, Ives's sense of humor is present in the form of an off-beat, off-key "Harvest Theme." The orchestra grows louder and louder to a sweeping climax. Suddenly a full chorus sings out:

> *O God, beneath thy guiding hand*
> *Our exiled fathers crossed the sea;*
> *And when they trod the wintry strand,*
> *With prayer and psalm they worshipped Thee.*

The first three movements of the *Holiday Symphony* were played as individual pieces on various occasions. The complete symphony was first performed by the Minneapolis Symphony, under the direction of Antal Dorati, on April 9, 1954.

A month later, on May 19, 1954, Ives died of a stroke. He is fondly remembered as "the father of American music" because he was the first American composer to be independent of European tradition. For Ives, it was O.K. to be American. In fact, it was great!

Henry Cowell, 1931
Stanford Archive of Recorded Sound

Chapter Four
HENRY COWELL
(1897–1965)

Imagine playing the piano with your fists and forearms. Or what if you reached inside the instrument and strummed and plucked the strings? Some people might think you were playing the piano improperly. However, if you were performing a piece composed by Henry Cowell, you would be doing it just right.

At the age of fifteen, Henry wrote one of his most famous piano pieces, "The Tides of Manaunaun." According to Irish legend, Manaunaun was the god of motion. He rocked the universe with great tides, moving all materials together to form the planets and stars. In "The Tides of Manaunaun," Henry wrote a beautiful melody accompanied by large groups of notes called tone clusters. Henry put so many notes in his tone clusters that he had to play them with his palm or forearm. The low, rumbling notes blend together to sound like Manaunaun's massive waves. Henry invented a new way to write music. He drew a line connecting the top note of a tone cluster to the bottom one, indicating that all the notes in between should be played. That made it easier for pianists to read so many notes at once.

Henry learned the story of Manaunaun and other Irish folk tales and songs from his father, Harry Cowell. Harry was born in Carlow, Ireland, and sailed to America when he was just a teenager. He eventually settled in San Francisco, where he tried to make a living as a writer. There he met another writer, Clarissa Dixon, a spirited feminist and a native of Illinois. Both Harry and Clarissa wrote about liberal ideas that were not generally accepted.

Harry was twenty-seven years old and Clarissa was forty-two when they married in Oakland in 1893. Their only child, Henry Dixon Cowell, was born on March 11, 1897, in a two-room cottage that Harry built in nearby Menlo Park. Besides writing, Harry worked as a printer. Clarissa was a full-time writer. Usually they didn't make enough money to make ends meet. What they couldn't give their son in material wealth, however, they made up in love and guidance. Henry once remarked that his parents told him, "Welcome and explore and inquire into everything, new and old, that comes your way, and then build your own music on whatever your inner life has been able to take in and offer you back again."

At the age of five, Henry began taking violin lessons. He progressed so rapidly that in two years he could play the difficult sonatas of Mozart and Beethoven. Harry was very proud and excited about his child prodigy and showed him off at every opportunity. Henry played for Harry's friends, music lovers, and patrons.

In 1904, Harry and Clarissa divorced, although they remained close friends. Clarissa shortened her first name and changed back to her maiden name, becoming Clara Dixon. She and Henry moved many times in the next several years. In each new place, Clara hoped that her writing career would take off. But things got a lot worse before they got better.

At one point Clara and Henry moved near the Oriental district of San Francisco. It was there that Henry first heard Chinese and Japanese children sing the folk songs of their native countries. Henry eagerly absorbed this strange, wonderful music and never forgot it. It lay sleeping in his memory until it sprung to life in his compositions many years later.

Henry continued his violin study. His father arranged for him to play in many public recitals. This was too much of a strain for Henry. He developed a nervous disorder called chorea that caused the muscles of his face, arms, and legs to twitch. His doctor ordered him to stop playing the violin. At the age of eight, Henry's brief career as a violinist came to a sudden halt. He and his mother returned to a more peaceful life in their Menlo Park cottage.

After the great San Francisco earthquake of 1906, Clara and Henry moved to the Midwest to live with some of Clara's relatives. In Des Moines, Iowa, Clara became an editor of a women's page of a newspaper called *Successful Farming.* She enrolled Henry in school, but the experience was traumatic. He suffered another bout of chorea and was allowed to stay home.

Clara and Henry then moved to New York City. Clara sold a novel to a publisher. The book was not successful so Clara didn't make much money on it. Next she took a job as caretaker of a house that was being renovated. At age nine, Henry climbed the scaffolding built around the house and wrote his first composition.

Clara wasn't able to sell any more of her writing. Harry sent them some money, but it wasn't much. One day, a friend visiting Clara and Henry found them both in bed, ill from malnourishment. They had to accept food and clothing from the Society for the Improvement of the Condition of the Poor.

The members of the Society didn't want to support anyone if they could find someone else to do it. They discovered that Clara had relatives who owned a farm in Kansas and sent her and Henry there. Clara and Henry weren't happy in their roles as poor relations. They would have preferred to go back to California, but the Society only provided fare to Kansas.

Farm labor was hard on Clara and Henry, both of whom were still in poor health. Clara's relatives had no interest in the arts and ridiculed her every time she sat down to write. Finally, after a year and a half, she sold a story and made enough money for her and Henry to return to California.

They found their cottage in shambles, but they fixed it up and moved in. Henry was allowed to roam the nearby hills and discover the world on his own. He enjoyed taking long walks. Later, as a young man, he would hike hundreds of miles along the coast of California, camping under the stars and eating whatever he could find. Henry was interested in all nature, especially insects. He collected them and studied them closely.

Henry found many ways to earn money to support his mother and himself. He cleaned chicken coops, tended plants, and herded cows. He worked as a janitor for a school, a job that paid five dollars a month. He sold some of his best insects to the Biology Department at nearby Stanford University. Henry also earned money in the Psychology Department at Stanford. A famous psychologist there, Dr. Lewis Terman, was developing the first IQ tests. Dr. Terman was especially interested in Henry because he didn't attend school. He wondered if that would make the boy less or more intelligent. Dr. Terman paid Henry fifty cents an hour to take his tests several times a week. After giving Henry all his tests, the psychologist came to the conclusion that Henry possessed all the characteristics of a genius.

One remarkable trait of Henry's was his hearing. He was able to sing scales consisting of tones that exist *in between* the keys on a piano. The keys on a piano are arranged in half steps. Henry could sing quarter tones.

By the time Henry turned thirteen he had saved sixty dollars, enough to buy a piano. Henry's piano was delivered one spring day after the rainy season. Horse-drawn carts and buggies had left deep ruts in Henry's unpaved street. One of the wheels of the delivery truck slipped into a rut. The piano fell off the back and broke into pieces. Henry was extremely disappointed, but not for long. A piano technician came out to his house and put the piano all back together. Supposedly, it worked just fine.

At last Henry could play the music that he had heard only in his mind. He began taking piano lessons from a neighbor in exchange for tending his garden. Henry composed many pieces at that piano, including "The Tides of Manaunaun."

On March 12, 1912, he made his debut as a com-poser-pianist in the Fairmont Hotel in San Francisco. The program consisted of all his own compositions. The people who attended Henry's performance had never seen anyone play the piano with his arms and fists and were quite shocked. Henry's tone clusters created a minor scandal.

After that recital, Henry performed whenever and wherever he could in the towns and cities near his home. Once Henry rented a little hall and invited some people to come hear his music. The night of his performance was stormy and very cold. Only one old man attended the concert. After Henry played his entire program for the single listener, he asked the man why he had come out in such bad weather. The man said he had to because it was his job—he was a music critic.

When Henry was a little older, he gave another memorable performance at a party in San Francisco. His host was Ansel Adams, a piano teacher and struggling pianist who later became a renowned photographer. Henry poked fun at some classical music. He played an excerpt from Wagner's *Tannhauser* with the aid of a wisk broom and a Chopin Étude assisted by an orange. According to one witness, Henry's arrangements were quite suitable for the music, even though they were a little strange.

By 1913, Henry had written over one hundred compositions. Harry took him around to various musicians hoping they could offer him guidance. Charles Seeger, a composer who taught at the University of California at Berkeley, immediately recognized Henry's talent. He had Henry enroll in music courses at the university and gave him private composition lessons. Seeger was first Henry's mentor, and later, his close friend. Henry introduced Seeger to his future wife, Ruth Crawford.

Besides composing, Henry also wrote about music theory. In 1916, he began writing *New Musical Resources*. It was the first American book on innovative ways to compose music. Dr. Samuel Seward, an English professor at Stanford University, helped Henry put his ideas down on paper. Henry finished his book in 1919, but it wasn't published until 1930.

Henry tried to study composition at the Institute of Musical Art in New York City. His teacher, Frank Damrosch, didn't like Henry's new ideas. He tried to get Henry to abide by rules that were hundreds of years old. Even when Henry used the rules, Damrosch returned his assignments covered with critical red marks. Henry retaliated by handing in a composition that had actually been written by the great seventeenth-century master J.S. Bach. When Damrosch returned that assignment with just as many red marks, Henry demanded a refund of his tuition. He returned to California to continue his study with Charles Seeger. Before long he became an assistant music professor at the University of California.

In 1918, Cowell enlisted in the army and served for the last year of World War I. At first he worked as a cook, but then he formed a band. He became the conductor of the band and arranged music for it to play.

After the war, Cowell went to New York City to give concerts and compose. In 1923, he got another idea to use in his piano compositions. He discovered that he could create new sounds on the piano by plucking, strumming, and sweeping the strings. To play his composition, "Aeolian Harp," Cowell silently pressed down certain keys, then reached inside the piano and swept his hand across the strings, much like a guitarist strums his instrument. Playing the piano in this manner makes it sound like an autoharp or zither.

For another one of his compositions called "The Banshee," Cowell stood beside the piano and swept the strings many different ways. He had an assistant hold down the damper pedal while he played so that all the strings could vibrate and echo inside the piano cabinet.

Cowell named his eerie scraping sounds well. According to Irish folklore, a banshee is a female spirit whose appearance warns a family that one of its members will soon die. The banshee is uncomfortable in the material world and wails until she is safely back in her spiritual one. According to Cowell, the older your family, the louder your family banshee will wail, for she has had that much more practice at it.

Also in 1923, Cowell toured Europe for the first time. While making his concert debut in Leipzig, he ran into trouble. He had only been playing a few minutes when some people in the audience got angry with him for playing the strings inside the piano and for pounding the keys outside with his fists. They shouted at him to leave the city immediately. Some other concertgoers defended Cowell. They said he should be permitted to play his concert, even if his music did sound awful. People from both sides of the debate leaped across the footlights and onto the stage. They broke into a fist-fighting brawl around the piano. Cowell continued to play, however, wondering why the people who disliked his music didn't just leave.

The police soon arrived and arrested twenty people. Cowell continued his concert, but some members of the audience hissed and booed after each selection. The next day, a music critic wrote in the paper, "Henry Cowell, an American pianist, gave a concert last night that had nothing to do with music."

This didn't discourage Cowell from giving concerts. He made four more tours in Europe and several in America within the next ten years. Cowell made many friends in Europe, including the famous composers Béla Bartók, Arnold Schönberg, and Alban Berg.

Cowell became well aware of the fact that most concertgoers only liked music they were familiar with. They were satisfied to hear the same music over and over. New music was rarely performed or published. Cowell decided to do something about that. In 1927, without any financial backing, he established *New Music Quarterly*, a journal devoted to publishing the works of modern composers. Cowell sent nine thousand letters throughout America and Europe asking music lovers, libraries, and schools to subscribe to his journal. Seven hundred subscriptions of two dollars each were returned to Cowell. With the fourteen hundred dollars he collected, Cowell published the first issue of *New Music Quarterly*.

Half of the subscribers didn't like the music Cowell published and promptly canceled their subscriptions. However, Cowell did receive a supportive letter from another composer, Charles Ives. Not only did Ives compliment Cowell's journal, but he also enclosed a check for twenty-five additional subscriptions. Cowell met Ives a few months later in New York and the two musicians began a lasting personal and professional relationship. Ives, a wealthy insurance man, funded many of Cowell's efforts to get new music published and performed. In 1931, he gave financial backing to the Pan American Association of Composers. This association sponsored two tours through Europe so that Europeans could hear American orchestral music.

In 1928, Cowell became the first American composer

Henry Cowell and Charles Ives were life-long friends
From the Charles Ives Papers in the Music Library of Yale University

to be invited to appear in the Soviet Union. At first, the Committee of Russian Composers thought Cowell's music was too radical; however, the students at the Moscow Conservatory soon changed the minds of Committee members. The students asked Cowell to repeat his works so many times that his concert lasted four hours. The Committee of the Russian Composers then recommended that Cowell's compositions be published. Two of Cowell's piano pieces became the first compositions by an American to be first published in Russia.

Cowell didn't limit his search for new sounds to just the piano. Later in his life he told a magazine reporter that when he and his wife went out shopping, they often struck things in the stores to see what sounds they made. In his "Symphony Number Eleven" Cowell used a set of four Pyrex bowls.

In 1925, Cowell wrote a piece called "Ensemble" for stringed instruments and thunder sticks. A thunder stick is a musical instrument that Southwest American Indians use in ceremonial dances. It is a one-foot to one-yard-long stick with a strip of leather attached to one end. A thunder stick is played by whirling the leather piece over one's head. The sound it makes varies from a purr to a roar, depending on how fast it is twirled. During the first performance of "Ensemble" one of the leather pieces flew off its stick and nearly hit a music critic. This was an accident, of course, but Cowell's friends kidded him about it. They claimed that he was trying to get even for all the bad reviews he got by killing off a critic. Although "Ensemble" was published, it wasn't performed again for nearly forty years. And when it was again performed, the thunder sticks were replaced with bamboo wind chimes. Nobody was taking any chances.

Besides creating new sounds, Cowell was also very interested in rhythm. He didn't think the rhythm in classical music was very interesting. A whole note can be divided into two half notes that are played twice as fast, four quarter notes played four times as fast, eighth notes played eight times as fast, sixteenth notes played sixteen times as fast, and so on. Cowell thought this traditional system of rhythm was missing out on a lot of possibilities. Instead of just dividing a whole note in half, then in half again and again, Cowell wanted to be able to divide it up many other ways. He wanted to divide a whole note into fifths, sevenths, thirteenths, and any other number he could think of.

There was no way to write these rhythms, so Cowell decided to invent one. Instead of just using ovals for note heads, Cowell used triangles, squares, diamonds, and rectangles. In 1917, he wrote a piano piece called "Fabrics" using his multi-shaped notes. He also wrote two other similar works in 1917 and 1919 called *Quartet Romantic* and *Quartet Euphometric*. *Quartet Romantic* is written for two flutes, a violin, and a viola, and *Quartet Euphometric* is for a string quartet. These pieces are so rhythmically complex that Cowell thought they were humanly impossible to play and that they would only be heard in his own mind. However, in 1964, a part of *Quartet Romantic* and all of *Quartet Euphometric* were played by the Galimir Quartet. Today, musicians are used to playing complex rhythms because so many modern composers use them. But when Cowell was writing them, they were almost unheard of.

By 1931, Cowell was still experimenting with complicated rhythms, even though he didn't think musicians could perform them. He dreamed up a keyboard instrument that could play sixteen different rhythms in sixteen different pitches. Cowell called his new instrument idea a rhythmicon. He asked Leon Theremin, a Russian electric engineer who was visiting the United States, to build the rhythmicon for him. Meanwhile, Cowell composed a piece for rhythmicon and orchestra called *Rhythmicana*.

The rhythmicon turned out to be a disappointment. It could play the rhythms just as Cowell wrote them, but the tones it produced were strange beeps and burbles that were not very pleasing to hear. Charles Ives paid Theremin to build an improved rhythmicon—one, Ives hoped, that would sound "nearer to an instrument than a machine." The tone quality of the second rhythmicon was better, but still unsatisfactory. Cowell never heard his symphony for rhythmicon and orchestra played.

Forty years later, composer Leland Smith programmed a computer to play the music written for the rhythmicon. On December 3, 1971, six years after Cowell's death, Sandor Salgo conducted the Stanford Symphony Orchestra in the first performance of *Rhythmicana*. That performance proved that Cowell was way ahead of his time. He wrote electronic music long before the technical means to play it existed.

In 1931 and 1932 Cowell lived in Berlin, supported by a Guggenheim grant. He was working in ethnomusicology, the study of music of different cultures of the world. Cowell studied the music of Asians, Orientals, and American Indians.

When he returned to the United States, Cowell became the director of musical activities at the New School for Social Research in New York. He and Charles Seeger taught classes in the appreciation of modern music and the ethnic music of many countries.

In 1936, Cowell met with the worst misfortune of his life. He was arrested in California on a morals charge involving an unnamed seventeen-year-old boy. Whether or not Cowell was actually guilty is not known. Probably if the young man had been a young woman, Cowell wouldn't have been accused of any crime. Besides that, the evidence against him was mostly circumstantial or falsified. A district attorney told him that he would get off easy if he pleaded guilty to a lesser charge. Cowell made the mistake of following the district attorney's advice. Without a trial or lawyer, Cowell was given the maximum sentence. He was sent to San Quentin Prison with the depressing thought that he might be spending the next fifteen years of his life there.

Cowell's spirit was not crushed, however. He was still devoted to music, whether he was in prison or not. He continued to study and compose music, he gave music lessons to his fellow inmates, and he organized a band.

Composers and musicians all over the country were outraged by Cowell's incarceration. They wrote letters to the State of California pleading for his release. Finally, after serving four years, Cowell was paroled to composer/pianist Percy Grainger. Cowell moved to

Great Plains, New York, to be Grainger's secretary. He was pardoned by the State of California in the spring of 1941.

Happiness followed on the heels of Cowell's prison years. On September 27, 1941, he married Sidney Hawkins Robertson, a musician, writer, and an ethno-musicologist whose special area of interest was hymns and folk songs of early America. Together, she and Henry wrote many articles and the book *Charles Ives and His Music*, published in 1956. Today it is still the most important biography ever written about Charles Ives.

Besides sharing the same interests as Henry, Sidney brought tranquility and balance to his harried life. She was the greatest influence on his later years. The Cowells bought a modest, clapboard house in Shady, New York, in the Catskill Mountains. Henry's and Sidney's home was surrounded by a pine forest filled with birds and other animals. In this lovely setting, Cowell wrote many articles about music and composed many works. During this time Cowell earned his living lecturing at various universities, including Stanford, Columbia, and Northwestern.

Again, Cowell took an entirely new direction in his composing. He completed his third symphony in 1942, and in the following years he wrote seventeen more. Sidney's interest in early American music inspired Henry to include traits of American hymns and folk tunes in his symphonies. The spirit of the jigs, reels, and ballads of his Irish heritage also found their way into his symphonies. Cowell recalled the Oriental folk songs of his childhood and also included their exotic flavor in his music.

During World War II, Cowell held the position of senior music editor of the overseas division of the Office of War Information. It was Cowell's job to choose what music was played over the American shortwave music broadcasts.

During the war, Cowell was also given an unusual assignment. The Shah of Iran wanted his soldiers to rise every morning and do a set of physical exercises called "Walter Camp's Daily Dozen." The Shah felt his men would be more enthusiastic if the exercises were set to Persian rhythms. When the Shah asked President Roosevelt to recommend someone to compose musical accompaniments for the exercise, the President immediately contacted Cowell. Cowell dashed the music off in a few days. Thousands of records were pressed and shipped to Iran.

In the fall of 1956, under a Rockefeller Foundation grant, the Cowells toured ten countries, including Ireland, Germany, Turkey, India, and Japan. At the request of the state department and by special invitation of the Shah, the Cowells spent the winter in Tehran. While there, Cowell supervised the new radio station. Fascinated by the Persian music he heard, Cowell wrote *Homage to Iran* and *Persian Set*.

The winter in Iran was hard for both Henry and Sidney. Upon their arrival in Pakistan, they both checked-in at a hospital. They were soon released and were able to continue their tour.

The music of Japan offered Cowell further inspiration. He wrote a piece called *Ongaku*, which means "the art and science of sound." This work is a unique blend of Japanese and Western music and is considered to be one of Cowell's greatest works.

In the last decade of his life, Cowell finally enjoyed recognition, honor, and financial security. Unfortunately, he was plagued with poor health. He suffered a series of strokes and a bout with cancer. Still, Cowell worked in music with as much enthusiasm as ever.

The year 1962 marked the fiftieth anniversary of his debut as a composer and his sixty-fifth birthday. Telegrams containing messages of congratulations poured in to Cowell, including one from President John F. Kennedy. Many concerts of his music were given in his honor with renowned orchestras playing his works.

Up until the day of his death on December 10, 1965, Cowell continued to compose and attend concerts of his music. Among his last works were two concertos for orchestra and koto, a Japanese stringed instrument similar to a zither. He was planning to write a twenty-first symphony when he passed away in his home in Shady.

Henry Cowell's life work can best be summed up in his own words: "I place no limitations of period or place on the musical materials I may wish to draw on, for the meaning of music does not depend upon the materials themselves . . . I have always wanted to live in the whole world of music . . . I have more ideas than I can ever use. This is a happy state and I wish the same to all of you."

Ruth Crawford Seeger
Used by permission from Michael Seeger

Chapter Five
RUTH CRAWFORD SEEGER
(1901–1953)

In the past, women had few opportunities to compose music. Composers used to be tradesmen, just like carpenters and tailors, and few women had occupations outside of caring for their families and households. Women were expected to be good amateur musicians— only good enough for playing and singing in the home. Consequently, the instruction they received was usually poor. Most weren't able to study with important composers or travel to the cultural centers of Europe to hear the best musical performances. With few exceptions, men shunned female composers because they didn't think women had the intelligence to write music. Women who wanted to get their music performed had to live a public life, and that went against the rules of society. For many years, women who appeared on stage were considered to be immoral.

Despite these obstacles, women did compose. Some female composers were only famous during their lifetime, then their music was forgotten. Some of this music is now being rediscovered, published, and performed. Today there are many women composers whose works are being played by leading orchestras and other musicians.

Ruth Crawford Seeger was an American composer who lived during the first half of this century. Like Charles Ives and her friend Henry Cowell, she was ahead of her time. She discovered startling new techniques of musical composition that other composers did not use until several decades later.

She was born Ruth Porter Crawford on July 3, 1901, in East Liverpool, Ohio. Ruth's mother was Clara Graves Crawford, the daughter of a strict Methodist minister. Clara had wanted to take piano lessons when she was a child, but her father thought it was a waste of money. When Clara left home at age sixteen to take a teaching job, she bought herself a pump organ and learned to play it. She made sure her daughter had the thing she missed the most in her own childhood. When Ruth was six, her mother sent her to a local piano teacher to start lessons.

Clara's husband was also a Methodist minister, but he was just the opposite of her father. The Reverend Clark Crawford was a quiet and friendly man who liked to tell his children, Carl and Ruth, stories. He was assigned to duties at many churches in Ohio, Missouri, and Indiana. As a result, Ruth lived in many different towns during the first eleven years of her life.

As soon as Ruth made new friends she had to leave them, but that didn't bother her too much. She liked to spend time alone—reading, practicing the piano, and writing in her notebook. At the age of seven she had already decided that she wanted to be a poet.

When Ruth was ten her family moved to Jacksonville, Florida. Ruth was a bright student and skipped several grades. She had little in common with most of her older classmates who were starting to get interested in dating, so Ruth spent even more time alone. Her father suffered from ill health for several years and died when she was only thirteen. Ruth's mother ran a boarding house to support herself and her children.

In high school, Ruth spent several hours a day practicing the piano. She read so much that Carl called her a bookworm. She was still determined to be a writer. One poem she wrote contained eight hundred couplets, or two-line rhymes. Her letters, stories, and diaries show that she was as talented in writing as she was in music. She was well-disciplined and set very high standards for herself. When Ruth was thirteen, she wrote in her diary:

> *And listen to me, Ruth. You will never make a success of yourself in this world, unless you learn to exercise your will power, and to tackle tasks which are to be done, not put them off. Suppose you are writing a book, and get a wee bit tired of it—for authorship is not all pleasure. How will you ever finish it if you have not trained your will power? Buckle to!*

Ruth's diary also indicates that she was often lonely. Like many people, she turned to her diary when she felt bad and had no one else to talk to. When Carl left home to join the army, Ruth wrote about her worry for him and all the other soldiers who were fighting in World War I.

After Ruth graduated from high school she wanted to study piano at a conservatory, but her mother couldn't afford to send her. Instead, Ruth taught piano at the School of Musical Arts in Jacksonville and directed a music program in a kindergarten. She continued to take piano lessons and practice. She composed simple pieces, but was frustrated by her lack of education in music theory. After three years, Ruth had saved enough money to begin college.

At age nineteen she enrolled at the American Conservatory of Music in Chicago, where she studied piano with Heniot Levy. She practiced many long hours. When her muscles got tired, she tensed them up and practiced harder. This caused her to develop tendonitis, which made her arms ache. Her music theory studies included classes in harmony, counterpoint, composition, and orchestration with Jon Palmer and Adolf Weidig. She also took music education classes and observed children's music classes. By the end of her first year of college, Ruth had earned a teacher's certificate.

During her second year at the conservatory, Ruth's tendonitis got worse. The more she tried to practice, the more it hurt. If she couldn't practice, then she couldn't take piano lessons. She began to wonder why she should even continue her expensive studies. On November 18, 1922, she wrote to her mother:

> *What am I gaining that is worth it all? . . . Again and again the debate has raged, and always peace and contentment come in the answer: my theoretical work. Yes, it alone is worth my being here. I feel myself broadening; my ear . . . is hearing better than it did last year. Tho we have not begun composition yet, I am working on little ideas that come to me.*

Ruth was already interested in composing, and the pain in her arms caused her to work more on composition and less on piano performance.

Ruth's money ran short in her second year of study. A relative was able to give her some financial help, but it wasn't enough. Ruth took a job as a coat checker in a theater in downtown Chicago. She was able to study on the job, and if the plays were good, she watched them. Ruth also began to teach private piano lessons.

After receiving her Bachelor of Music degree in 1923, Ruth decided to stay in Chicago and start work on her master's degree. She continued to study composition with Adolf Weidig and wrote *Five Preludes for Piano* in 1924 and 1925. Soon after, Ruth composed another four preludes for the piano. She also wrote *The Adventures of Tom Thumb* for piano and narrator, a composition for children. It won first prize in the Sigma Alpha Iota national composition contest.

Among Ruth's other compositions of this period are three suites for small groups of instruments and a violin sonata, all of which were never published. These early compositions show Ruth was influenced by Alexander

Scriabin and Claude Debussy. They also display her efforts to develop her own style. She tried to avoid the use of the scales and chords present in most classical music. Instead, she used unexpected leaps in her melodies and clashing harmonies.

In 1924 Ruth's mother came to live with her. The two women shared a small apartment until Mrs. Crawford died four years later. Ruth missed her mother for a long time. Mrs. Crawford had been proud of her daughter's accomplishments and had offered her companionship, encouragement, and support.

Also in 1924, Ruth began to take private piano lessons from Djane Lavoie-Herz. Madame Herz recognized the young composer's talent and introduced her to people who could help her career. Madame Herz became Ruth's mentor and good friend.

In the evenings, Madame Herz's North Chicago piano studio turned into a gathering place for the musical avant-garde. Musicians and composers came there to perform new works and discuss new methods of composition that were not yet accepted by the general public. During such a gathering, Ruth met Dane Rudhyar, a composer who was devoted to the music and bizarre mystic beliefs of the Russian composer Alexander Scriabin. It was probably Rudhyar who inspired Crawford to study the unique music theory of Scriabin's compositions.

Crawford often attended Madame Herz's soirees escorted by her friend Alfred Frankenstein. Nineteen-year-old Frankenstein played the clarinet in the civic orchestra and Crawford played in the percussion section. Later in his life, Frankenstein wrote music reviews for the *San Francisco Chronicle*, program notes for the San Francisco Symphony, and books about music. While many music writers were stuffy or snobby, Frankenstein had a witty, entertaining style.

Alfred Frankenstein's family was friends with the poet Carl Sandburg and his family. When Sandburg asked Frankenstein if he knew of a good piano teacher for his daughters, Frankenstein immediately suggested Ruth Crawford.

Sandburg greatly influenced Crawford's thinking. Most of his poetry reflects his interest in common people. He was active in fighting for the rights of the working class. Crawford admired Sandburg's poetry so much that nearly every text she set to music was written by him. Sandburg, in turn, loved the music of the American people. He collected folk songs in a book called *American Songbag*. He asked Crawford to write piano accompaniments for some of the songs included in the collection.

The most famous member of Herz's musical circle was Henry Cowell. He had surprised many audiences throughout the world. by playing the piano with his fists and elbows and reaching inside the instrument to strum the strings. He had organized concerts of new music and had tried to get the music published. Cowell was very impressed with Crawford's compositions and arranged to have her second set of Piano Preludes, numbers 6, 7, 8, and 9, appear in the October 1927 issue of his publication, *New Music Quarterly*.

Crawford finished her master's degree in 1927. She

spent the summer of 1929 composing at the MacDowell Colony in Peterboro, New Hampshire, where she could work without the usual interruptions of the outside world. In the fall, she was reluctant to return to Chicago. Cowell tried to talk her into coming to New York to study composition privately with his former teacher and friend, Charles Seeger.

Actually, Cowell had to talk Seeger into the idea, too. Seeger didn't believe that women could be composers because all the famous ones had been men. He thought Crawford would just waste his time. Cowell showed Seeger some of Crawford's compositions, but Seeger wasn't impressed. Cowell insisted that Seeger was just the influence Crawford needed to develop into a mature composer.

Eventually Cowell got his way. He arranged for Crawford to spend the winter in the home of Blanche Walton, a wealthy patron of American avant-garde music. Once Crawford began her study with Seeger, she soon convinced him of her worth as a composer.

"Rat Riddles" is the title of one composition Crawford wrote that winter that shows Seeger's influence. It is a song based on the Sandburg poem by the same name. Later it was included in a set called *Three Songs*. "Rat Riddles" is sung by a low woman's voice called an alto. The singer is accompanied by an oboe, piano, and four percussionists. Optional parts for a group of string players and a group of wind players are included in the score. One of Seeger's ideas that Crawford used in "Rat Riddles" was to place the strings and winds far apart from the rest of the musicians. Therefore, space became an important part of the music. The strings and winds create a whirling confusion of sound heard faintly behind the singer and other instruments.

In 1930 Crawford was the first woman to be awarded a Guggenheim Fellowship for European study. A short time before Crawford was to leave for Europe, her relationship with Seeger grew from a warm friendship into love. On the day she set sail from Quebec, they both had mixed feelings. They were excited about her opportunity to study abroad, but they were also sad about having to spend a whole year apart.

In Europe, Crawford had the opportunity to visit and exchange ideas with composers Alban Berg, Béla Bartók, and Maurice Ravel. During her stay in Berlin and Paris, Crawford composed "In Tall Grass," another setting of a Sandburg poem that is included in *Three Songs*. She also wrote her most well-known and admired work, String Quartet, 1931.

The first movement of the quartet has wide leaps in the melody and changing meters. Crawford uses some of the same material in the second movement, marked "Scherzo." *Scherzo* means "like a joke." It is played very lightly, but very fast. Charles Seeger called the slow third movement "an experiment in dynamic counterpoint." He meant that each instrument grows softer and louder at different times. The instruments play long, sustaining tones that blend together to create dark, moody harmonies.

In the fourth movement, which is marked "as fast as possible," Crawford pits the first violin against the other three instruments. The movement begins with the first violin playing a single note. After a rest, it plays two more notes, then three, then four. Each time the first violin enters, it plays a phrase one note longer than the previous phrase, until finally, midway through the piece, twenty notes are strung together. Crawford then raises the tones a half step and reverses the process. The first violin plays one note less each time it enters, until, at the end of the piece, it plays a single tone. Also, the first violin starts out very loud, then gradually becomes very soft in the middle of the piece, then grows louder until the end.

Meanwhile, the other three instruments do just the opposite. They start with a twenty-note figure that is shortened one note at a time until it is a single note in the middle of the piece. Then, increasing one note at a time, the figure grows to twenty notes again. These three instruments start very soft, grow very loud, then get very soft again.

Crawford's organization of notes in String Quartet, 1931 is almost as technical as plans for constructing a bridge. Intellectually the piece is interesting, but that isn't enough to make good music and Crawford knew it. The music stirs the emotions as well. In regards to Crawford's music, Charles Seeger wrote, "Serious music is a cooperation of head and heart, of feeling and thinking." In String Quartet, 1931, Crawford delights the listener by timing the entrances of the instruments in different ways. Sometimes the first violin and lower instruments answer each other very politely, waiting a few beats of silence in between. Other times, the two parts jump in on top of each other, causing the excitement to build.

After a year in Europe, Crawford applied for a renewal of her Guggenheim Fellowship. It was denied, probably because she didn't compose a symphony during her first year as a Guggenheim Fellow. She returned to New York in November of 1931 and composed "Prayers of Steel," the third song in the set *Three Songs*.

In 1932, Ruth Crawford married Charles Seeger. She had always hoped to have a family, and through her marriage got one that was already in progress. Charles, who was fifteen years older than she, was a widower and the father of three sons, Charles, John, and Peter. Peter later became known as Pete Seeger, the popular folk singer. The family grew when Ruth gave birth to Michael in 1933. Peggy was born less than two years later.

Ruth's musical life changed along with her personal one. The Depression of the 1930s caused many people in the United States to be jobless, homeless, and hungry. It bothered her that so many people were suffering while she composed a type of music that only a small elite group could appreciate. She wanted to write music that would have meaning to people who needed their spirits lifted.

Henry Cowell agreed with Ruth. He founded an organization called the Composers Collective, which was dedicated to creating such music. Charles Seeger wrote that the purpose of the group was "to connect music somehow or other with the economic situation."

Ruth composed two songs for the organization and titled them "Sacco, Vanzetti" and "Chinaman, Laundryman." She signed them "Ruth Crawford Seeger," using her married name for the first time.

Ruth Crawford Seeger didn't accomplish what she had hoped with these two songs. They had little meaning for most people. The Seegers and some of the other members in the Composers Collective soon realized that "the music of the people" didn't need to be composed. It already existed in the form of folk music. Folk music consists of easy-to-sing tunes with lyrics about the interests and problems of everyday life. However, little folk music was known outside of the region where it originated. The few published folk songs were written in a style that was not true to the way they were supposed to sound.

About this time the Seegers met John Lomax and his son Alan, two musicologists who had traveled throughout the United States in search of folk music. The Lomaxes had recorded people singing in fields, prisons, churches, and town halls. They asked Ruth to transcribe the folk music, or put it in written form, so it could be published in songbooks. She eagerly accepted the task.

The Seegers moved to Washington, D.C., where Charles became music advisor for the Resettlement Administration of the United States. Ruth found all the folk music that the Lomaxes had recorded stored on aluminum records in the Archives of the Library of Congress. She took them to an upper room of her home and began the work of transcribing them.

Many of the recordings were difficult to notate. The singers slid into pitches. When they sang sad songs or "the blues," they bent pitches downward or "went flat." This made it hard for Ruth to tell which notes to write down. Oftentimes background noise on the recordings made the singing difficult to hear. Ruth played the recordings slowly, fast, loudly, and softly. She played a single phrase over and over. Sometimes the phonograph played all day and far into the night. Ruth sang the songs, too. She couldn't stop herself from singing them because they were always going on in her head. Singing the songs helped her find the best way to notate them.

The Lomaxes sometimes disagreed with Ruth's transcriptions. They wanted her to write in all the sliding and bending of "blue notes." Ruth insisted on notating the music as simply as possible. She argued that the changes in pitch were in between notes on a musical staff and couldn't be written down anyway.

Ruth transcribed over two hundred songs and wrote piano accompaniments for many of them. These appear in the Lomaxes' book *Our Singing Country*, published in 1941. Ruth and Charles were co-editors for the Lomaxes' later book, *Folk Songs, U.S.A.*, which contains 111 songs. In the forward of this collection, the Seegers wrote that musicians singing folk songs should not speed up and slow down the songs or get louder and softer. These ideas are taken from classical music and aren't meant for folk singing. The Seegers also wrote simple piano accompaniments that help singers learn the melodies.

A dedicated nursery school teacher, Ruth Crawford Seeger felt American
folk music was the best introduction to music for preschoolers
Used by permission from Michael Seeger

Meanwhile, the Seeger clan continued to grow. Barbara was born in 1937 and Penny was born in 1943.
During the Depression it was hard to support such a
large family. Ruth taught private piano lessons for a
little extra income. When Barbara grew to preschool
age, Ruth taught music at four nursery schools and
helped organize the Silver Spring Cooperative Nursery
School in Maryland.

Ruth loved working with the preschoolers. She felt that folk music was just the right material for their music lessons. She made copies of the folk songs she transcribed, then she and her children cut and pasted them together to use as songbooks in the nursery schools. Later these materials were published. Some of Ruth's publications include *American Folk Songs for Children*, *Animal Folk Songs for Children*, *Christmas Folk Songs for Children*, and *Let's Build a Railroad*.

The Seegers' household was filled with the sounds of America's folk music from morning until night. After dinner, the family played and sang together. Peggy played the guitar, Mike played the autoharp, Ruth played several instruments, and everybody sang. Ruth

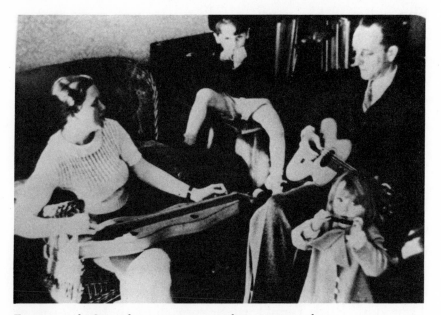

Evenings at the Seeger home were spent making music together
Used by permission from Michael Seeger

often played the piano after the children were settled in their beds.

In 1941, Charles was appointed chief of the music division of the Pan American Union. This appointment gave the Seegers the opportunity to learn the folk music of Central and South America. Ruth edited the music in *Folk Songs of the Dominican Republic*, which was published in 1955.

In 1939 she composed *Rissolty, Rossolty*, a piece for a small orchestra based on three folk songs that she transcribed. The work was commissioned by CBS for the children's radio program, "School of the Air."

For over ten years, Ruth did no composing. Like Charles Ives, she stopped composing at the time of her life when she should have been producing the most. She believed her work in folk music was more important than her own composing. Still, she had a tremendous urge to get back to it.

In 1952, when Penny turned nine, and the older children were either fully grown or required less care, Ruth finally had time to devote to her own composing. She wrote *Suite for Wind Quintet* in the style she developed before working in folk music.

In the summer of 1953, Ruth discovered that she had cancer. She began x-ray treatments, but they didn't help her condition. On November 18, 1953, she planned to appear at the *Washington Post* Children's Book Fair to promote her songbooks. She felt too sick to attend, so Michael and Peggy went in her place. That day, Ruth Crawford Seeger died in her home at the age of fifty-two.

Sidney Robertson Cowell, Henry Cowell's wife, had

fond memories of Ruth. She wrote, "For all her great creative gifts and wide musical knowledge . . . she had the widest possible sympathies, the quickest loyalty and kindness."

During her lifetime, Ruth Crawford Seeger wrote relatively few compositions, and these were nearly forgotten after her death. In the last twenty years, however, music theorists have been studying her works more and more. They have found her String Quartet, 1931 to be one of the most important works written for string quartet during the twentieth century. Today her works are being published, performed, and recorded. If she hadn't died so young, she may have become one of the most renowned composers of American music.

Ruth Crawford Seeger transcribed over six hundred songs and wrote piano accompaniments for three hundred of them. Her work helped make the folk music of America familiar to all of us. Today, Michael and Peggy, as well as Pete, continue the work that their parents began by singing folk songs and writing new songs and books about music.

Ruth Crawford Seeger worked very hard. She drove herself even more during her last several years. Peggy remembers it was "as though she was almost conscious that she was going to die early and wanted to get it all in before she went." Even so, Crawford Seeger left many of her projects unfinished. She had plans for several more songbooks and many more compositions. She was able to live up to her own motto: "We should not seek to become greater than others, but to discover the greatness in ourselves."

George Gershwin

Gershwin Archive photograph, courtesy of Edward Jablonski, Lawrence D. Stewart, and Mrs. Ira Gershwin

Chapter Six
GEORGE GERSHWIN
(1898–1937)

The Gershwin brothers were always called Ira and George, but those weren't their real names. George, born on September 26, 1898, was actually named Jacob. His older brother, Ira, born December 6, 1896, was named Isreal, but he didn't discover that until he applied for a passport at age twenty-four! It is funny that his parents never thought to tell him what his real name was.

George was born in Brooklyn, which in 1898, was much like the country, with wide, open fields to play in. The Gershwins, however, didn't spend much time in Brooklyn. When George was three, his family moved to the East Side of Manhattan. The Gershwins, in fact, moved around quite a lot. During his first eighteen years, George lived in twenty-eight residences; twenty-five were in Manhattan and only three were in Brooklyn. His father, Morris, changed jobs frequently, and liked to live close to work. He owned or managed bakeries, restaurants, Turkish baths, a cigar store and pool parlor, a rooming house, and even a bookmaking establishment where people placed bets on sporting events.

Morris was too easy-going and friendly to ever be very successful at any of his businesses but he always managed to support his wife, Rose, and their four children. Every once in a while, Rose had to pawn her diamond wedding ring to see the family through a hard spell, but she always got it back. Both Morris and Rose were Russian-Jewish immigrants and spoke mostly Yiddish, with a little English mixed in. Morris always had trouble understanding and speaking English. He thought George's song "Fascinating Rhythm" was "Fashion on the River." Rose had a passion for card-playing and enjoyed betting on the horses as much as Morris did. They often rented a limousine to attend the races, even if they couldn't afford it. Rose let her boys go their own way, but she always had a good idea of what they were up to. George was especially close to her and asked her advice through adulthood.

The East Side neighborhoods where the Gershwins lived were noisy and crowded. Vendors sold their wares from pushcarts. Gangs of boys played punchball, stickball, handball, and baseball among the horse-drawn wagons. Some of the kids were pretty rough. George, however, could roll with the punches, except for one, which broke his nose. While Ira pored over dime detective novels, some of which a young boy had no business reading, George became known as the roller-skating champion of the block.

George didn't care much for school. He rarely did his homework and often got poor grades. He misbehaved in class and played hooky whenever he thought he could get away with it. Numerous notes from his teachers were sent home to his parents; however, Morris and Rose saw very few of them. George talked his neighbors into forging his parents' signatures on several occasions. Sometimes he would even get Ira to appear at school as the supposed substitute for his parents. George wasn't dumb; he just thought school work was sissy stuff and he thought music was, too.

When George was about ten he heard something that changed his mind about music. He was sitting in his classroom when he heard the beautiful strains of a violin coming from the nearby assembly hall. The violinist was Maxie Rosenzweig, an eight-year-old prodigy who also attended Public School Number 25 and was playing for the younger grades. The boy would later be known as the brilliant virtuoso, Max Rosen.

George was so impressed by Maxie's playing that he waited for him after school in the pouring rain. After waiting for some time, George finally figured out that Maxie had left through another exit. He found out where the young musician lived and ran to his house.

Maxie wasn't home, but his parents were so pleased with George's admiration for their son that they arranged a meeting between the two boys.

Maxie and George became close friends. They shared secrets and wrote numerous letters to each other even though they were oftentimes together. They frequently talked about music. George said later in life, "Max opened the world of music to me." Even so, the young violinist didn't offer George any encouragement. Max bluntly told George that he could never be a musician because he lacked talent.

This didn't stop George from trying to pick out tunes on neighbors' pianos any chance he could get. One day Morris and Rose bought a secondhand piano on the installment plan so that Ira could take lessons. As soon as George saw the piano he amazed his parents by playing it. Ira didn't get much of a chance at the piano after that. George had already decided who the musician in the family was going to be.

George took lessons from a number of teachers in the neighborhood. One of his teachers assigned him opera music transcribed for the piano rather than the usual scales and piano pieces. George wasn't making much progress so he auditioned for another teacher, Charles Hambitzer. After George finished pounding out the *William Tell Overture*, Hambitzer said of George's previous teacher, "Let's hunt out that guy and shoot him—and not with an apple on his head, either."

Hambitzer was so impressed with George's talent that he refused payment for his lessons. He gave George the music of Chopin, Liszt, and Debussy to play. George was more interested in pop and jazz, but Hambitzer insisted he study the basics first. George did not rebel. In fact, he admired his teacher so much that he rounded up ten neighborhood kids and convinced them to also take lessons from him.

George wrote his first two songs at the age of fourteen but they were never published. That summer, he worked as a pianist in a Catskill mountain resort for five dollars a week. By then it was obvious to his parents that music was the most important interest in his life; however, Rose wasn't convinced that George could earn a living at it. She suggested that he enroll in the High School of Commerce, where he could learn to be an accountant.

George's study habits didn't improve. By the end of the year he was failing most of his subjects. In May of 1914 he asked his mother if he could quit school to go to work as a professional musician. She gave him permission. Soon after, George was hired at Remick's Music Publishing House, becoming at age sixteen the youngest pianist working in Tin Pan Alley.

No one knows how the long row of music publishing houses in Manhattan came to be called Tin Pan Alley. Perhaps it was because of the tinny sound of so many pianos going at once, "plugging" the newly published music. The publishers could make thousands of dollars on one song, but only if it was a hit. In order to make the song popular, it had to be heard by many people. There wasn't any radio or television in 1914. The only way people heard popular tunes was by attending the vaudeville shows, nightclubs, and theaters. The publishing houses therefore hired many pianists to "plug" their wares.

From eight to ten hours a day, George and his fellow pluggers sat in cheap, tiny rooms called parlors and played newly published songs. Singers, actors, and comedians searching for new material for their acts would come hear the pluggers. Many of the performers had little musical background. Sometimes George would have to teach a song to a performer by playing it over and over. The job could get very monotonous, but George made it interesting by arranging the same piece in a slightly different manner every time he played it. He experimented by adding new chords and runs and changing the tempo. George got very good at transposing music from one key to another so that any singer, whether his or her voice was high or low, could sing any song.

By working for a music publisher, George thought he had his foot in the door when it came time to publish his own songs. He was wrong. When he submitted one of his own songs to Remick's, it was flatly rejected. George was told that he had been hired as a plugger, not a songwriter. This didn't discourage him, however. He continued to write songs and eagerly played them to anyone who would listen. Many of the songs that he wrote during this time weren't published until later in his life.

One of George's songs, "When You Want 'Em, You Can't Get 'Em, When You've Got 'Em, You Don't Want 'Em," was finally published in 1916. Sophie

Tucker, a famous "red-hot mama," heard the song, liked it, and asked Harry von Tilzer to publish it. The lyricist for the song, Murray Roth, was paid an advance of fifteen dollars. George turned down his advance, imagining he would received a big lump sum in royalties later on. After a good amount of time had gone by, he asked von Tilzer for his royalties. The publisher handed George a five-dollar bill. That was all he ever received for the song.

Though working as a plugger didn't further his career as a composer, it made George a better pianist. Soon he was known as the best pianist at Remick's. This led him to another job—making piano rolls. Player pianos and the rolls used in them were tremendously popular since they were the only way nonmusicians could hear music in their own homes. Everyone in a family, including the children, enjoyed pumping the pedals, watching the piano keys press down magically, and listening to popular tunes.

George began to attend recording sessions on Saturdays in New Jersey. His modest salary was five dollars per roll or twenty-five dollars for six rolls. Between 1915 and 1926, George recorded over a hundred rolls under many different names—Fred Murtha, Bert Wynn, and James Baker, to name a few—for many different labels. The companies thought the people would buy more piano rolls if they had a variety of pianists to choose from. Imagine someone arguing that Fred Murtha was a much better pianist than Bert Wynn when they were both George Gershwin!

George left Remick's after a little less than two years.

He began to think that the music written for vaudeville performers was boring and trite. George preferred to listen to the works of Irving Berlin and Jerome Kern, whom he admired very much. He decided that the best songs were written for musical theater. George dreamed of hearing his own songs sung on Broadway.

Gershwin got a job as rehearsal pianist for the musical *Miss 1917*. He was paid thirty-five dollars a week, much more than his job at Remick's. More important than the money, however, was the experience he gained. He was able to watch how a musical comedy was put together. Once the play and music were written, the show was rehearsed over and over. Some of the play was rewritten. Some of the songs were taken out and others were added. Gershwin began to see what worked on stage and what didn't. He kept this in mind when it came time to write his own musical.

Meanwhile, Gershwin kept writing songs. Some of them got put into shows that needed extra material, and some were sung by famous stars. Max Dreyfus, head of T.B. Harms, perhaps the most important publishing company in Tin Pan Alley, heard two of Gershwin's songs and was very impressed. Dreyfus had a gift for recognizing talented composers early in their careers. He offered Gershwin thirty-five dollars a week just to write songs and submit them to Harms for possible publication. He also promised to pay Gershwin a royalty of three cents for each copy of his songs that sold. This was a very generous offer and Gershwin gladly accepted it. It meant that he could spend less time as a pianist and more time composing.

In 1918, George wrote a song called "The Real American Folk Song." It was the first time he collaborated with lyricist Arthur Francis, who was really George's brother Ira. Ira had been working at odd jobs while struggling to become a writer. Thus far, he had sold only one short story for a dollar and had written vaudeville reviews for free. Ira created his pen name by combining the names of his younger brother, Arthur, and his sister, Frances. He used a pen name for his songs because he didn't want people to think he was trying to break into lyric writing by using the Gershwin name. He wrote lyrics to many songs before using his real name.

George got paid very little for the songs he wrote. He knew that in order to receive a large share of royalties, he had to write a complete musical. He got that chance in 1919 when he composed all the music to the show *La La Lucille*. The musical got good reviews and was fairly successful. However, five years went by before Gershwin got a chance to write another complete score.

In 1919, Gershwin also wrote his first hit song, "Swanee." He got the idea from Stephen Foster's song "Swanee River." Al Jolson recorded "Swanee" on one of the first phonograph records made. The records reached far more listeners than live entertainers ever had. As a result, George made $10,000 on record and sheet music sales. Before long he became a celebrity and met many important people.

One of his new friends was Jules Glaenzer, an executive of a jewelry company named Cartiers. Glaenzer introduced Gershwin to many celebrities, including Charlie Chaplin, Fanny Brice, and the famous brother-and-sister dancing team, Fred and Adele Astaire, who later starred in several Gershwin musicals. Glaenzer tactfully tutored Gershwin in social graces so that he would be more appealing to all the important people he met. Glaenzer taught Gershwin to remove the cigar from his mouth when he was being introduced to a lady, to not wolf down his food, and to dress fashionably. In 1923, Glaenzer invited Gershwin to stay in his home in Paris. He showed him all the sights and introduced him to many European musicians and artists. Gershwin loved Paris. His visit there inspired him to write his orchestral work *An American in Paris* several years later.

Back in New York, Gershwin attended many parties, often escorting beautiful show girls, usually a different one each night. One special woman never did win George's heart, though he had a close friendship with Kay Swift, a songwriter who was already married. George was too preoccupied with his music to offer much in a relationship with a woman. Ira, as usual, was just the opposite. He met Leonore Strunsky at a party in the early 1920s and married her on September 14, 1926. The couple never had any children, though they lived happily together until Ira's death in 1983.

At parties, Ira quietly sat in a corner while George took his place at the piano. He sang and played his latest show tunes while the other guests listened appreciatively. Once George's mother suggested that he not play so much at parties. George replied that he wouldn't have a good time if he didn't. Whether in a crowd or alone, George loved to improvise at the piano. He never played any of his songs the same way twice, always experimenting with new harmonies and arrangements.

After coming home late from parties, Gershwin would often compose until dawn. He usually began a new work by improvising. His fingers moved swiftly over the keyboard, magically drawing beautiful tunes out of nowhere. He had little intellectual knowledge of harmony and couldn't sight-read music very well. Though he tried to study with various teachers off and on during his life, he never had the discipline to stick with structured learning. He had an exceptional ear, however, and could immediately play on the piano any sequence of chords that he heard aloud or in his head. He knew what notes were the right ones to use in his compositions once he played them on the piano. He once admitted, "Composing at the piano is not a good practice. But I started that way and it has become a habit." As a result, all the music he wrote, whether it was for musical comedy, symphony orchestra, or opera, sounded like his unique piano-playing style.

In the same year that Gershwin wrote "Swanee," he also wrote a simple piece for string quartet called "Lullaby." It shows that Gershwin knew very little about writing for stringed instruments and that he didn't quite know how to develop a tune into an instrumental piece. Gershwin also made a weak attempt at writing opera. He composed a one-act opera called *Blue Monday Blues*, which centered around three tragic characters in black Harlem. It was a miserable flop, although that wasn't all Gershwin's fault. The opera was performed by white singers wearing heavy black makeup. They looked like comedians cast in dramatic roles. A review in the newspaper stated, "a soprano finally killed her gambling man. She should have shot all her associates the moment they appeared and then turned the pistol on herself." Though "Lullaby" and *Blue Monday Blues* were not successful, they show that even early on Gershwin had ambitions beyond writing musical comedy.

A few years later, Gershwin got an opportunity to turn his ambition into a dream come true. Paul Whiteman, a famous dance band leader, wanted jazz to gain more respect in the musical world. He thought many sophisticated listeners were unwilling to go to dance halls and nightclubs to hear jazz so he decided to bring it to them in a concert hall. In late 1923, he asked Gershwin to write a jazzy composition for orchestra and solo piano for which Gershwin himself would appear as the guest soloist. Gershwin eagerly agreed; however, since he was very busy composing for Broadway and since no date for the concert was set, he didn't begin work on the project immediately.

Late on the night of January 3, 1924, George was shooting billiards with a friend in a Broadway parlor when Ira came rushing in, clutching the early-morning edition of the *New York Tribune*. Excitedly, he showed George an article that stated that George Gershwin was "at work at a jazz concerto" for a concert Paul Whiteman planned to give the following month!

Spurred into action, George began work on his *Rhapsody in Blue* on January 7. Since he had no experience in writing a long orchestral piece and little time to do it, Gershwin decided not to use a standard classical form. Instead, he allowed one musical idea to flow freely into another, the way most rhapsodies are constructed. He also wrote the piece for two pianos—one piano represented what the soloist would play and the other one was for the orchestra part. Ferde Grofe, a skilled musician who often arranged music for Paul Whiteman's band, rewrote the second piano part so that the orchestra could play it. Gershwin finished his two-piano version of *Rhapsody in Blue* in approximately three weeks. Grofe took another ten days to orchestrate it. The musicians rehearsed for five mornings in a dingy nightclub cluttered with spilled drinks, full ashtrays, and other debris that the evening customers left.

Paul Whiteman billed his concert as "An Experiment in Modern Music." He spent a lot of money on advertising and gave away many tickets to important musicians and music critics, including the famous composers Sergei Rachmaninoff and Victor Herbert and violinist Jascha Heifetz. On the night of the performance the auditorium was packed with people, including many that were standing. It was hot and stuffy and the concert was very long. Actually, the program was neither very "experimental" nor "modern." It consisted mostly of Broadway hits by composers like Jerome Kern and Irving Berlin that were arranged to show off Whiteman's band. *Rhapsody in Blue* was second-to-the-last on the program, and by then many disappointed listeners were scurrying toward the doors and some fresh air.

The people that stayed, however, had the thrill of hearing music-making history. Gershwin's hands flew wildly over the keyboard as Whiteman's band played more exuberantly than it had the entire evening. They finished *Rhapsody in Blue* to thunderous applause. Gershwin reappeared on stage over and over, taking countless bows.

The success of his first orchestral piece was above and beyond Gershwin's greatest expectations. In the next ten years, *Rhapsody in Blue* earned him a quarter of a million dollars. Whiteman and Gershwin recorded the work twice. It was adapted for ballet and included in a movie. Grofe reorchestrated the work for symphonic orchestra in 1926 and 1942. The 1942 version is the one orchestras use today. *Rhapsody in Blue* has become one of the most frequently played American orchestral works.

Also in 1924, George and Ira Gershwin wrote the complete score and lyrics to the hit show *Lady, Be Good,* starring Fred and Adele Astaire. From this show on, Ira wrote the lyrics for nearly all of George's songs.

George contributed to several other shows in 1924 and 1925. He wrote a show called *Primrose* for the London stage, and he and Ira wrote another Broadway hit called *Tip-toes.* Still, George was eager to get back to composing for orchestra. His next opportunity came when the New York Symphony Orchestra commissioned a piano concerto for which Gershwin was to again appear as the soloist. Once the contract was signed, Gershwin had to find out what a concerto was. He also bought a textbook on how to compose for all the instruments of the orchestra. For this piece, Concerto in F, he wanted to write the orchestration himself.

Once Gershwin studied up on concertos, he again chose to write in a free form rather than a classical style. When he had completed the work, he hired an orchestra of sixty musicians to try it out. This was extremely expensive, but Gershwin didn't care. This was the first piece he had written for orchestral instruments and he wanted to be sure it sounded right no matter what it cost. He asked his friend Bill Daley to conduct. Walter Damrosch, the conductor of the New York Symphony, was also present at the tryout. After hearing Concerto in F and talking it over with Daley and Damrosch, Gershwin revised the piece quite a lot. Among other changes, he cut out nearly a hundred measures that he thought were too repetitious. When the work premiered in Carnegie Hall, the audience was very enthusiastic. The critics, however, were cool. Nevertheless, Gershwin played Concerto in F with many other symphony orchestras after that. The work gained in popularity over the years and is frequently performed today.

Beginning in 1926, Gershwin became an art collector. Over a period of years he purchased 144 exceptional works by Gauguin, Picasso, Chagall, and others. He paid about $50,000 for a collection that would be worth millions today. Gershwin took painting lessons from his cousin, artist Henry Botkin. He got so caught up in painting that for a while he considered giving up composing to concentrate on becoming an artist. He never did this, and it is fortunate that he didn't. Though his paintings show that he had a talent for line, color, and form, they don't possess the strong imprint of his personal style that all his music does.

Gershwin wrote two more smash hits for Broadway, *Oh, Kay!* and *Funny Face,* as well as the controversial satire on war, *Strike Up the Band.* He was then ready to write for orchestra again. He remembered how much he had enjoyed Paris during his 1923 visit and thought up the title *An American in Paris.* For this work, Gershwin was more ambitious than ever. He decided to eliminate the piano part and his own playing, both of which contributed to the success of *Rhapsody in Blue* and Concerto in F. Perhaps that is why he had trouble getting started on the work. He decided to revisit Paris to get inspired. He spent nearly four months there during the spring and summer of 1928.

Gershwin brought back to New York four French taxi horns and many new ideas for *An American in Paris.* Again he used a free form for this long, single-movement work. Included in it are three "walking" themes that depict an American touring the city—a Charleston theme in the snappy rhythm of that popular dance of the 1920s, a "taxicab" theme, and a blues theme. Gershwin's progress as a composer of orchestral music is apparent in his more varied use of rhythm, texture, modulations, and orchestration. Besides the four French taxi horns, he used three saxophones, an instrument that was new to the symphonic orchestra.

In 1928, George moved away from his family, but he took Ira with him. George rented a luxurious seventeenth-floor penthouse and Ira and Lee moved in next door. Besides being his favorite lyricist, Ira was also George's constant companion and business manager.

Two years later, when George was asked to write the score for the movie *Delicious*, it was no surprise that Ira and Lee moved out to California with him. The movie studios were so rich that many of the writers, composers, and actors lived on fat salaries for doing little work. George was no exception. He filled in his many leisure hours with the sports he most enjoyed—golf, tennis, horseback riding, and skiing. George was, in fact, very proud of his tanned, muscular physique and was not above flexing his muscles or posing before a mirror. Always the opposite, Ira tended to be pudgy and sedate.

Ever since the flop of *Blue Monday Blues*, Gershwin had been determined to write a successful full-length opera based on the lives of poor blacks. In 1926, he read the novel *Porgy* by DuBose Heyward and was certain that he had found the right story for his opera. *Porgy* is about a group of blacks living in a poor part of Charleston called Cabbage Row, which Heyward fictionalized to "Catfish Row." The story is centered around Porgy, a crippled black man, and his persistent love for Bess, a beautiful but weak-willed woman who gets involved with the wrong men—Crown, who is a bully, and Sporting Life, a dope dealer. When Crown commits murder and goes into hiding, Porgy is the only person willing to take Bess in and care for her. They are happy together for a short time, but then Sporting Life steals Bess away, promising her a better life in New York. The story ends with Porgy hitching his goat to his little cart, preparing to make the long journey to New York in search of Bess.

After reading *Porgy*, Gershwin contacted Heyward. The author was enthusiastic about collaborating with Gershwin on an opera but he was already writing a play based on *Porgy*. Gershwin and Heyward therefore decided to write the opera version at some later date. As always, Gershwin was busy with many other projects. It wasn't until 1934 that he and Heyward communicated again. At that time, Al Jolson also expressed an interest in a musical version of *Porgy*. Heyward asked Gershwin if Jolson could star in the opera, but Gershwin was not in favor of it. He had learned from his earlier mistake of using white performers in blackface makeup and insisted on using black actors and singers. Heyward also suggested that they use some spoken dialogue, but Gershwin wanted all the words to be sung, as in traditional opera.

In the summer of 1934, Gershwin moved to a two-room cabin on Folly Beach, a small island ten miles from Charleston. The accommodations were quite different from his Manhattan penthouse. The weather was hot and humid and only bottled water was available for drinking. Sand crabs invaded his living room and chirping crickets nearly drove him crazy when he was trying to get to sleep at night. These discomforts didn't matter much to Gershwin, for at Folly Beach he could observe the people he was writing about. They were

George and his brother Ira wrote many hit songs together
Gershwin Archive photograph, courtesy of Edward Jablonski, Lawrence D. Stewart, and Mrs.
Ira Gershwin

much different from the sophisticated black entertainers that he knew in New York. These people did little
mixing with the white population and were therefore
able to retain much of their own customs, folklore,
and music. Gershwin was also able to work closely with
Heyward and compose for long stretches of time without the usual interruptions that he experienced in New
York.

In the fall, Gershwin returned home with much of
the opera done. Heyward had finished the libretto. He

and George asked Ira to help put the final touches on the lyrics. Heyward once said, "The brothers Gershwin, after their extraordinary fashion, would get at the piano, pound, wrangle, sweat, burst into weird snatches of song, and eventually emerge with a polished lyric."

Gershwin and Heyward decided to call the opera *Porgy and Bess* so that it wouldn't be confused with the play *Porgy*. When it came time to find producers, they had difficulty in obtaining financial backing. George, Ira, and Heyward finally invested a total of $70,000 of their own money on the production, thinking that they would earn a large return on their investment. George had earned his share of the money by writing and starring in a weekly radio show called "Music by Gershwin." Though he had earned a high salary, he resented the show because it took so much time away from composing *Porgy and Bess*. As a result, the score was not completed until September, 1935.

Gershwin personally auditioned the singers and orchestra players. The singers had to be coached in using the quirky Cabbage Row dialect. One singer couldn't read music so his part had to be taught to him by rote. The opera opened in Boston and later ran on Broadway to enthusiastic audiences. Gershwin called his work a folk opera, since he derived much of his style from the music of the blacks that he observed during his stay in South Carolina. Critic Francis Perkins of the *New York Herald-Tribune* hailed the work as "a notable achievement in a new field." Another critic, however, complained that it wasn't much more than a Broadway show. Another one wrote that singing all the lines slowed down the action. This hurt ticket sales and *Porgy and Bess* closed after a disappointing 124 performances. The Gershwins and Heyward lost much of the money they had invested. However, this did not discourage George. He recorded and published many of the songs from *Porgy and Bess* and earned a nice profit in this manner. He was certain the critics were wrong about *Porgy and Bess* and was planning a West Coast revival of the production at the time of his death. Many successful revivals of the opera have since been produced in this country and all over the world, both with and without spoken dialogue.

One contributing factor to the poor receipts from the premiere run of *Porgy and Bess* was the Depression of the 1930s. During the 1935–36 season, at least fifty fewer productions were presented on Broadway than in the year before, and most of them did not earn a profit. After losing money on *Pardon My English* (1933), *Let Them Eat Cake* (1933), and *Porgy and Bess*, Gershwin was reluctant to invest his valuable time in another Broadway show. The real gold mine for composers, writers, and entertainers was now in Hollywood. Though live theater and most other businesses were suffering, the motion picture industry was booming. People all across the nation, many of whom were out of work and had little food on the table, flocked to the movie theaters where they could forget their troubles for a couple of hours for the small price of a nickel.

In August 1936, George and Ira landed a movie contract and rented a Spanish-style home in Beverly

Hills, complete with a swimming pool and tennis court. The Gershwins socialized with many of their friends from New York who had also moved to California, and they made many new friends as well. George frequently played tennis with Arnold Schönberg, the famous German composer who invented twelve-tone music.

Between movie assignments, George performed many concerts. On February 11, 1937, he played his Concerto in F with the Los Angeles Philharmonic. During the performance he had a lapse of memory during which he thought he could smell the odd odor of burning rubber. Though his blunder was hardly noticeable to the audience, Gershwin was very upset about it. Nothing like that had ever happened to him before. A doctor gave him a thorough examination but could find nothing physically wrong. Gershwin attributed the incident to fatigue. He stopped worrying about it until May, when he started experiencing severe headaches and dizzy spells. Through the month of June he became more feeble. He could barely eat and could not tolerate sunlight. He couldn't walk unassisted and he lost much of his coordination.

On the morning of July 9, he asked his doctor if he could play the piano, which he managed to do with some of his old finesse. That afternoon he fell into a coma. A spinal tap revealed that he had a brain tumor that had to be operated on immediately. The tumor was removed on July 11, but Gershwin died five hours later without ever regaining consciousness.

News of Gershwin's death filled the music world with

shock and sadness. Over four thousand people attended two simultaneous funerals, one in Hollywood and the other in Manhattan, where his body had been shipped.

Gershwin left as his legacy nearly a thousand popular songs, more than a dozen musicals, several fine orchestral works, and one of the most important American operas. He was the first American composer to successfully write both popular and concert music. Not a day goes by without thousands of Americans playing or singing music by George Gershwin.

Milton Babbitt
Used by permission from Milton Babbitt

Chapter Seven
MILTON BABBITT
(1916-   )

When Milton Babbitt was three years old, his picture and an article about him appeared in a Lincoln, Nebraska, newspaper. The article boasted that he had been able to identify recordings of classical music since the age of two. Milton could also tell the sum of his mother's grocery bill by mentally adding her purchases when she returned from the store. While these two feats made whimsical reading material, they also revealed the young boy's remarkable gifts in both music and mathematics.

Milton Byron Babbitt was born May 10, 1916, in Philadelphia. His mother, Sara Potamkin, a native of Philadelphia, enjoyed popular music. His father, Al-

bert, was a Russian-born mathematician who appreci-
ated Italian and Russian operas and symphonic works,
but could not read music. Milton's father taught mathematics in Lincoln during World War I and for a few
years afterward. The family then moved to Jackson,
Mississippi, where Milton grew up.

At the age of four, Milton began to study violin. He
made his debut at age five, playing the second movement of J.S. Bach's Concerto for Two Violins with
piano accompaniment at the institute for the blind.
Milton was very proud of the fact that he had memorized his part. To be sure that the audience was aware
of it, he stood far away from the other soloist, who
used music.

That same year, Milton's teacher showed him the
violin part to the Mendelssohn Violin Concerto in E
Minor. The work inspired Milton to write his first
composition, a violin solo that he entitled *Violin Concerto*. A concerto is usually written for solo instrument
and orchestral accompaniment; however, since Milton
was given only the solo part of the Mendelssohn work,
he assumed that all there was to a concerto was a single
instrumental part.

Also at the age of five, Milton entered public school,
beginning in the second grade. "I soon learned the
social limitations of the violin," says Babbitt, "which
was not welcomed in dance bands." He quit the violin,
hoping to take up the trumpet. Louis Pello, an Italian-
born conductor who taught almost every instrument,
lured Milton into studying clarinet by calling it the

"violin of the band." Soon Milton also took up the alto and soprano saxophones.

Playing B-flat, E-flat, and concert or C-pitched instruments caused Milton some confusion. He possessed the rare gift of perfect pitch, meaning that he can sing any note asked for or identify any note he hears. His teacher could not explain transposing instruments well enough for Milton to understand it. For years he would say to himself, "That is a 'C' I hear; but is it a 'C' on the violin, or clarinet, or saxophone?"

During every summer of his childhood, Milton and his mother traveled to Philadelphia to visit her family. Milton's most memorable summer was in 1926 when he was ten. The city was celebrating the 150th birthday of the Declaration of Independence, which Thomas Jefferson had written in Philadelphia. As part of the festivities, the Philadelphia Orchestra gave dazzling performances, including Brahms's Symphony No. 3.

Milton's uncle, Frank Potamkin, was a pianist who was studying at the Curtis Institute of Music. He was friends with Philadelphia composers Marc Blitzstein, Isador Freed, and Paul Nordoff, whom he introduced to his young musical nephew. Milton's uncle played the works of Scriabin, Stravinsky, and Schönberg for him. About Schönberg's music, Babbitt recalls, "Its only immediate effect was to mystify me, but I never forgot that first aural encounter." Later, Schönberg's work would have tremendous influence on Babbitt's own composing.

When Milton returned to Jackson that fall, his parents bought him a piano and gave him lessons. His formal training in piano lasted a very short time, however, because his "playing by ear" made his teacher angry. In those days, some teachers had the ridiculous idea that picking tunes out by the way they sounded would prevent a student from learning to read music. Today, most teachers think playing by ear helps students develop musically.

At the age of twelve, Milton wrote the music and lyrics to a song he called "That's Why I'm Blue." He entered it in a song-writing contest sponsored by the well-known band leader Paul Specht. Milton won first place. He also returned to the violin, but never enjoyed it much. He used it mainly to learn string quartet works.

Throughout his school years, Milton played in marching bands, concert bands, orchestras, and pit orchestras for shows. His favorite kind of music-making was with dance bands, that imitated the style of Guy Lombardo and other famous band leaders. For these he wrote many songs and made arrangements of other composers' music.

He subscribed to *Metronome, Variety, Billboard,* and *Étude,* trying to learn all he could about music and show business. His favorite radio program was Rudy Vallee's "Fleischman Yeast Show," which introduced new and obscure show tunes. If one of Milton's rehearsals ran past seven o'clock, he made his mother sit before the radio and write down the titles of the songs he had missed hearing. Milton would then dash out to buy the sheet music, hoping to be the first in Jackson to perform the new tunes.

When Milton graduated from high school at age fifteen, he was spending almost all his free time with music. His father felt strongly that he should attend a school of music, but Milton didn't want to. Even at his young age he had already seen enough struggling musicians to know such a life was not for him. Besides, he was tired of practicing other people's music. He didn't realize that there were other things he could do in music besides perform the works of other composers.

In 1931 Milton took a summer job at Harms Music Publishing Company in Tin Pan Alley in New York City. There he worked for Max Dreyfus, the same man who had helped Gershwin get his start in song writing.

That fall Milton wanted to go to Tulane University because he thought it would be exciting to live in New Orleans. However, the university would not accept his application because he was too young. His parents gently suggested that he attend the University of Philadelphia so that his relatives could look after him. Milton majored in mathematics, but continued to compose on his own. He also played in different kinds of bands. In one dance band, he performed with David Raksin, who went on to write the famous pop tune *Laura*, and many other songs.

Milton's Uncle Frank and his older cousin Lloyd Fisher, who was then in graduate school, noticed how much time he spent in music without receiving college credit. Like Milton's father, they urged him to major in music. A book published in 1933 called *Twentieth Century Music* also helped Milton decide to study music. In the book, author Marion Bauer discussed new and avant-garde trends in music, including Arnold Schönberg's twelve-tone music, also called tone row and serialism.

Babbitt enrolled in New York University's Washington Square College because Bauer taught there. "By the time I entered NYU in February, 1934," Babbitt recalls, "I was devoted to the music of Schönberg."

Schönberg, a Jew, escaped from Nazi Germany and arrived in New York in October 1933. Babbitt expected to study with him during the school year of 1934–35. His plans fell through when due to poor health, Schönberg moved to California in the summer of 1934 and joined the music faculty at UCLA. Babbitt did meet Schönberg a few times in 1934 and in the late 1930s. Later, Babbitt came to know Schönberg's widow very well. He is still a close friend of members of Schönberg's family.

After graduating with a B.A. in music in 1935, Babbitt was not eager to go on to graduate school. He says, "I, who was to become not just admittedly but proudly an 'academic composer', swore never to have anything further to do with an academic institution." Instead, he hoped to study privately with composer Roger Sessions, who would begin teaching at Princeton University that fall.

One day in late summer, Babbitt tucked his student compositions under his arm and sought out Sessions in his attic room, three or four flights above some piano studios on East Sixty-first Street in New York City. Sessions greeted him curtly at the door, led him down a narrow path between two large grand pianos, and sat on his bed to study the prospective student's work. Babbitt recalls, "He then asked me why I wished to continue to study, and with him; when I responded that I desired to begin from scratch, to reconsider and redo everything from the beginning, he appeared pleased."

Sessions did indeed start Babbitt at the beginning. At the first lesson Sessions opened his Beethoven Piano Sonatas to the first sonata and began taking it apart note by note. Sessions also gave assignments that Babbitt describes as "those threadbare but nasty exercises [which] seemed to violate all principles of direct musical engagement." Eventually, however, Babbitt saw the purpose in doing them.

While studying with Sessions, Babbitt spent two years reviewing concerts for a Chicago publication called *The Musical Leader*. The only payment he received was free concert tickets. However, the job gave him an opportunity to hear all the music he had missed while growing up in Mississippi. It was the best kind of supplementary study he could get.

Babbitt worked under Sessions watchful eye for three years. The instructor gave the direction and the freedom that the young composer desired and needed. Unlike most composer-instructors, Sessions did not try to make Babbitt imitate his style. Sessions, in fact, had many talented pupils who went on to develop their own unique styles.

In 1938, Sessions invited twenty-two-year-old Babbitt to join him on the music faculty at Princeton even though he had earned only a B.A. Babbitt received his Master of Fine Arts degree from Princeton in 1942.

On December 27, 1939, Babbitt married Sylvia Miller, whom he had met at New York University. Sylvia had a graduate degree in sociology and worked in Washington for the government during World War II, and later in New York as a market analyst. Milton's and Sylvia's daughter, Betty Ann, was born on August 20, 1946.

Milton Babbitt began his pioneering work in electronic music as early as 1939. Engineers at the David Sarnoff Labs at RCA, located in Princeton, tried to help him produce sound by means of hand-written sound tracks. Imagine trying to get a tape recorder or computer to "understand" hand-written commands today; yet, in 1939, that was the most promising medium.

World War II interrupted Babbitt's early attempts to produce music electronically. During the war years he taught mathematics at Princeton, which allowed him no time to compose.

After the war, Babbitt did not want to return to teaching music immediately; instead, he composed a film score. He also composed the music and some of the lyrics for a musical comedy called *Fabulous Voyage*. The show was never produced, although three of the songs were published. By working on these projects, Babbitt learned that the physical and mental pressures of show business were not for him. He returned to the music faculty at Princeton.

He was then ready to get back to composing serious

music. Concerning this time in his life, Babbitt writes, "My prewar works seemed many stages removed from me, and therefore I 'retired' them; I had, so to speak, 'thought' myself through a whole compositional phase during the war period, with no works to show for it."

Babbitt was still very much interested in the logic of Schönberg's twelve-tone system. Schönberg had developed it in the early twenties. However, twenty-five or so years later it was still a new and highly controversial idea. No one in music, it seemed, had wishy-washy feelings about serialism; they were either passionately for it or against the twelve-tone system. Babbitt felt that Schönberg had started a revolution in music.

During the three hundred years before Schönberg came along, pitches or tones were structured within a system called tonality. In tonality, groups of seven pitches form families, or keys. The pitches within a key, ordered from the lowest to the highest, form a scale. The first note of the scale is called the tonic and is so important that most tonal music begins, and more importantly, ends "on tonic." The second most important pitch in a key is the fifth note of the scale, which is called the dominant because it "dominates" the key. The other pitches in the key have different roles of lesser importance, and so do the pitches that are outside the key. Tonality, then, is a hierarchy similar to the way chess pieces are ordered: tonic, like the queen, is the most powerful, the dominant, like the bishop, is second, and so on.

Bach, Beethoven, Wagner, and other composers, each used tonality in a new way, stretching its limitations a little farther in each era. Schönberg thought that tonality had been taken as far as it could go. He thought it was time to throw out the tired old ruling hierarchy and replace it with democracy. His twelve tone system treated all twelve pitches equally. Before composing each piece, Schoenberg ordered the twelve pitches in a different way, a device he called a tone row. As he composed a piece, he tried to go through the tone row, using all the pitches in order, before using the first pitch in the row again.

Schönberg knew he couldn't use the twelve pitches in the same order over and over for an entire piece any more than Beethoven would use a single seven-note key for an entire symphony. Schönberg then figured out three ways to vary the tone row: retrograde, or backward; inversion, or upside-down (a jump *up* from one pitch to the next in the original row would be the same-sized jump *down* in the inversion); and retrograde-inversion, or backward and upside-down. The row could also be transposed or begin on any of the twelve pitches. With these variations, the original row could be used forty-eight different ways. The possibilities of tone combinations are therefore many times greater in the twelve tone system than in tonality. A composer using twelve-tone could discover a melody or harmony he would never think of when using tonality.

Some people who didn't like the idea of twelve-tone, also called serialism, thought that any composer using it would sound like Schönberg. Twelve-tone, however, is not a style, but a technique. The styles of Schönberg and his two most important students, Alban Berg and Anton Webern, are all unique. Igor Stravinsky's twelve-tone pieces sound like Stravinsky's other works, just as Aaron Copland's twelve-tone pieces sound similar to Copland's other music.

Babbitt was also interested in developing his own twelve-tone style. He got the idea to take serialism a step farther than Schönberg. "The twelve-tone set," he reasoned, "must absolutely determine *every* aspect of the piece." Babbitt was the first composer to use this concept of total serialism, though European composers Karlheinz Stockhausen and Pierre Boulez discovered it independently soon after him.

Babbitt thinks that all elements of the composition can be controlled by the tone row or, to use his term, *set.* He carefully selects a set, then applies it to rhythm, timbre (different musical instruments), register (low and high), dynamics (loud and soft), and articulation—which includes the attack (the beginning of a tone) and decay (the dying away of a tone). He does this by taking the intervals or distances between pitches and mathematically converting them to distances in time to create rhythms and degrees of loudness to create dynamics. Most composers use only eight levels for dynamics from *pp* (very soft) to *ff* (very loud). Babbitt has broadened the range from *pppp* to *ffff*, creating twelve levels of volume to correspond with the twelve tones of the set.

Babbitt first used his total serialization technique in three compositions: "Three Compositions for Piano" (1947), "Composition for Four Instruments" (1947–48), and "Composition for Twelve Instruments" (1948).

"Composition for Four Instruments" is written for

*Milton Babbitt composing on the RCA Mark II Synthesizer at the
Columbia-Princeton Electronic Music Center*
Used by permission from Milton Babbitt

flute, clarinet, violin, and cello. It is one movement
but can be divided in fifteen sections. Each section is a
different combination of instruments. The instruments
trade off very rapidly. Sometimes an instrument jumps
in to play only a single note. All the melodic ideas are
very short. The opening clarinet solo, for instance, is
based on a three-note unit.

Because Babbitt demands so much precision in all
elements of music, musicians have great difficulty play-

ing his compositions satisfactorily. Frustrated by poor performances of his music, Babbitt returned to the exploration of producing music through electronic means.

During the mid-1950s, engineers at the RCA David Sarnoff Laboratories were trying to build an electronic instrument for sound synthesis. Babbitt became aware of their efforts and worked as a consultant on the project. In 1959 the RCA Mark II Synthesizer was developed. It was moved to the Columbia-Princeton Electronic Music Center in New York City and Babbitt became a co-director of the center.

The RCA Synthesizer takes up an entire wall at the center. It has little or nothing in common with what is now called a "synthesizer." It can't be performed on like a piano or organ. Its only keyboard is similar to a typewriter. The composer uses it to punch his musical instructions onto a wide roll of paper that is fed into the synthesizer. The composition produced may then be recorded on tape. This eliminates the use of other musicians to perform the music. The RCA synthesizer is highly complicated and only a few other composers besides Babbitt have used it. It takes several hours to produce several minutes of music. Babbitt also writes all his synthesizer work in traditional notation by hand.

Babbitt has used the RCA Synthesizer to compose all his electronic music. In 1960–61 he composed "Composition for Synthesizer," which was the first piece produced entirely on the Mark II. He also composed "Ensembles for Synthesizer" in 1964 and "Occasional Variations in 1975."

In using the synthesizer for "Composition for Synthe-sizer," Babbitt was not interested in creating weird new sounds. "Nothing," he says, "becomes old as quickly as a new sound." Listening to the work, you will hear a few noiselike sounds: hissing, rattling, pops, and beeps. Other timbres are similar to traditional instruments, like plucked strings, orchestra bells, gongs, pitched drums, organ, and bassoon. However, it is quite obvi-ous that the tone color is produced electronically. Rhythm is measured in seconds and minutes rather than in beats and measures. You won't feel like tapping your toe to the music. Babbitt uses gonglike chords and melodic fragments that jump from high to low pitches and change speed. The same melodic ideas are played backward and upside-down. The texture be-comes thicker and thicker as the number of melodic lines increase from one to four.

"I have lived through so many bad performances of my music," Babbitt once said, "that I must confess I look forward to walking into the electronic studio with my composition in my head and walking out with the performance on the tape in my hand." Still he has no intentions of giving up traditional ways of making music. He is interested in increasing the ways to create music, not eliminating them.

As a result, Babbitt has worked with the concept of combining electronic music with live performers. This is a very satisfying combination because the synthesizer accurately plays the complicated rhythm and pitch materials while the live performers breath life into the music. In order to perform these pieces, the synthesizer part is placed on tape, which is then used to accompany live musicians in concerts. Pieces in which Babbitt has combined synthesizer with live musicians include *Vision and Prayer* (1961), *Philomel* (1964), and *Phonemena* (1975) for soprano and tape; *Correspondences* (1966–8), for string orchestra and tape; and *Reflections* (1975), for piano and tape.

The partnership of soprano and tape works well and many electronic music composers have used it. In *Phonemena*, Babbitt does not set a poem or other kind of traditional text. Instead, he uses phonemes, the smallest sound units of speech. He uses twenty-four consonant sounds and twelve vowel sounds, numbers chosen to correspond with the twelve tones in his set. The voice part has many leaps and quick passage work with many kinds of articulations. The soprano's voice is lilting and warm and gives us a feel for the beat. Skipping through the phonemes gives a whimsical effect; it sounds almost as if parts of words have been bleeped out. The synthesizer accompaniment adds other melodies, rhythms, and timbres. The contrast between human and machine adds yet another dimension to the work.

Babbitt has also written a version of the work that uses piano accompaniment instead of tape. It is interesting to compare the two versions, however—the piano version is not as effective. The pianist can't be as precise as the synthesizer can, and a piano has only one timbre while a synthesizer has many. Either way, *Phonemena* is an extremely difficult piece to sing, and in thanks to the few vocalists who have been successful,

Babbitt dedicated the work: "To all the Girl Singers I have Known."

Babbitt also continues to write for traditional instruments without the use of any electronics. These compositions include *Partitions* (1957) and *Post-partitions* (1966) for piano; *The Widow's Lament in Springtime* (1950) and *The Head of the Bed* (1982) for voice and instruments; *All Set* (1957) for jazz ensemble; *Relata I* (1966) and *Relata II* (1969) for orchestra; Concerto for Piano and Orchestra (1985); *An Elizabethan Sextette* for women's chorus (1978); and "Composition for Guitar" (1984).

Some people have said they don't like Babbitt's music, calling it "mathematical," "ultrarational," and even "scientific." They say it is too thought-out or intellectual and not emotional enough.

In response to people who criticize his music, Babbitt wrote an essay entitled "The Composer as Specialist." (The essay is also known as "Who Cares If You Listen?", a title that *High Fidelity* magazine used without Babbitt's permission.) "The time has passed when the normally well-educated man without special preparation could understand the most advanced work in mathematics, philosophy, and physics," wrote Babbitt. "Advanced music . . . scarcely can be expected to appear more intelligible than these arts and sciences . . ." Babbitt goes on to say that experimentation in music must continue, even if only a few listeners like the results. Otherwise, Babbitt writes, "Music will cease to evolve, and, in that important sense, will cease to live."

Actually, linking math with music is a very old idea. Pythagoras of ancient Greece discovered that objects vibrate in mathematical ratios to produce the different pitches. In the Middle Ages, math and music were taught as a single subject. Also, any musical relationship can be expressed mathematically.

Babbitt has written much about his musical process and is on the editorial board of the periodical *Perspectives of New Music*. As the founder of the "Princeton school of composition," he has influenced many composers, including Eric Salzman, Donald Martino, Andrew Mead, and Charles Wuorinen. Babbitt retired from Princeton in 1984 and now teaches at the Juilliard School of Music. He is still a director-emeritus of the Electronic Music Center, though he no longer uses it for his own compositions. His last work with synthesizer was *Images*, for saxophonist and tape, written in 1979. Babbitt and his wife live in Princeton. He continues to compose and lecture throughout the country and world.

George Crumb
Used by permission from Pach Brothers

Chapter Eight
GEORGE CRUMB
(1929–   )

◆

George Crumb has invented a whole new world of sound and a unique orchestra to play it. He uses traditional musical instruments, but they are played in imaginative ways. He asks a pianist to drop a chain over the strings so that they rattle like a snare drum. A harpist threads the strings of the instrument with paper. Singers wail, whisper, and trill their tongues.

Crumb uses musical instruments that are not usually members of a symphonic orchestra. He has taken instruments from children's rooms, including a toy piano, a slide whistle, and the pure, high voice of a boy. He has borrowed instruments from American folk music and other cultures, including the dulcimer, mu-

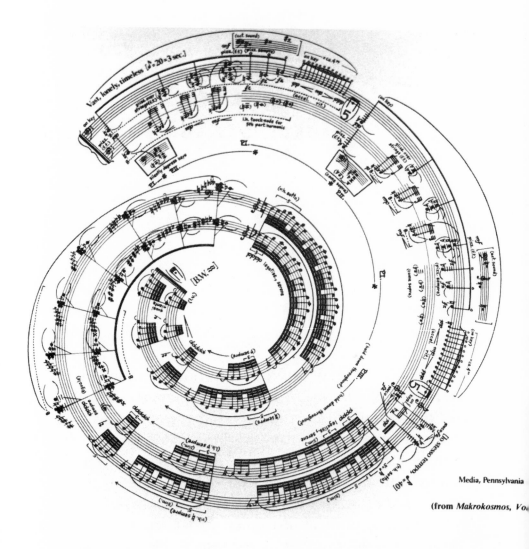

Crumb's handwritten scores are so interesting to view that some people hang them on their walls as art

"Spiral Galaxy" copyright 1974 by C. F. Peters Corporation. Used by permission

sical jug, musical saw, banjo, harmonica, sleigh bells, sitar, and African log drum. He also uses pot lids, iron chains, sheets of metal that roar like thunder, and crystal goblets that are tuned by the amount of water each one contains.

In many instances, Crumb requires musical instruments to be electrically amplified. However, he is one of the few modern composers who doesn't compose electronic music for tape recorders, synthesizers, and computers. He always has plenty of ideas for creating new sounds with traditional instruments. He also thinks the human performer brings expression to the music-making process.

Crumb's musical language even looks foreign on paper. Several staves may twist and bend into a single staff like tributaries pouring into a river. Other staves spin into spirals or curve into circles. Two staves may even form the shape of a cross. Crumb's musical calligraphy is so interesting to view that some people place pages of his scores in frames and hang them on their walls like art.

At first glance, some musicians might be puzzled by Crumb's style of notation. They might shake their heads and think that they will never figure out what he means. However, with further study they discover that the composer's intentions are quite clear. Jan De-Gaetani, a soprano who frequently performs George Crumb's music, wrote this about his scores: ". . . the page is always glorious to look at. It is intended to excite and stimulate. One wants to learn this music, to ask questions, to understand the gestures. It makes the whole process of learning and practicing such a pleasure."

George Crumb's unique world of sound grew out of a very traditional background in music. His father, George Henry Crumb, Sr., was a clarinetist. As a boy George Sr. played in the "Crumb Family Orchestra," performing at summer resort hotels around the Cincinnati area. As an adult, he worked at many musical jobs. He was the principal clarinetist in a symphony and played in a dance band. He conducted a Shriner's band and a movie theater orchestra that accompanied silent films. He was a music copyist and arranger. Sometimes he wrote down songs he heard on the radio and arranged them in a new way. His favorite music was the classics, which he performed in a chamber group.

The composer's mother, Vivian Reed Crumb, was from Chehalis, Washington. She played the cello in the Charleston Symphony for twenty-five years, acting as principal much of the time. In all those years she never missed a single concert.

George Henry Crumb, Jr., was born on "Black Thursday," October 24, 1929, the day of the big stock market crash. His brother, William Reed, was born February 26, 1932. The boys grew up in Charleston, West Virginia, near the Kanawha River. They had happy childhoods in spite of the hardships of the depression.

George, nicknamed "Bun," was a quiet boy who only felt comfortable with his family and a few close friends. He liked to roam in the nearby hills and hold stone-throwing contests at the river. The Crumbs lived in a big Victorian house in which the octagonal music room was the center of activity. George and William heard a lot of music inside and outside of their home.

The Crumb boys often attended the Shriners' band concerts conducted by their father. George thought the bold brassy sound of John Philip Sousa marches was very exciting. Mrs. Crumb took the boys with her to symphony rehearsals and concerts. George also heard West Virginian country and gospel music. This music inspired him to use the harmonica, musical saw, musical jug, and banjo in the pieces he composed much later.

At the age of seven, George began taking clarinet lessons from his father. He started on the high E-flat clarinet because his hands were too small for the more common B-flat clarinet. Two years later he took a few lessons on the piano. George was more interested in making up his own tunes than practicing his lessons. Whenever he got annoyed or frustrated he stalked into the music room and began improvising on the piano. Sometimes he opened the lid of the old upright to explore the inside of the instrument. Later he would compose pieces requiring the performer to play inside the piano.

At age fourteen, George began to study the piano more seriously. He discovered that he liked it more than the clarinet. He progressed very rapidly and was soon playing difficult works by Beethoven and Mozart.

Meanwhile, William learned to play the flute. The Crumb family played a lot of music together. There is not very much music written for the combination of flute, clarinet, cello, and piano, so the boys' father rearranged the works of Mozart and Haydn to suit his family's needs. When George got to be a better pianist, he and his parents also played trios by Beethoven and Brahms.

When George was eleven his mother was surprised to find in his room some compositions that he had written. He was so shy and quiet that he had been composing without her knowing it. These early compositions were similar to the works of Mozart. Later, George also composed in the style of Beethoven, Chopin, and Debussy. He wrote a lot of music very fast. George's father encouraged his early attempts at composition. He helped him get his ideas down on paper by teaching him proper notation. He told him how each instrument of the orchestra was different from the others, then showed him how to write music especially suited for each one.

By the time George graduated from high school, he had composed about forty pieces. He had written piano pieces and many works for his family to play together. He had also written songs and choral music. Two of his larger works were performed by a local orchestra. George was very excited about hearing such a large ensemble play his compositions. He was amazed to discover that his music sounded much the way that he imagined it would.

In school, George earned barely average grades. He found that none of his subjects were as interesting as music. He much preferred reading books about Beethoven and Mozart than his textbooks. George also studied hundreds of orchestral scores from his father's library. Sometimes he followed the written music while he listened to records or symphonic broadcasts on the radio. He even took the scores to school and read them during class. He tried to imagine what they sounded like instead of paying attention to his teacher.

George's study habits didn't improve during his four years at Charleston High. Elizabeth May Brown, his first and only girlfriend, remembers that "teachers used to yell at George because he wore his hair long, was a terrible dresser, and composed music in English class."

George did have a few interests other than music. As a member of his high school track team he competed in the running broad jump and high jump. He also took up the unusual hobby of pyrotechnics, or developing homemade Roman candles and giant firecrackers. Once he blew off a neighbor's garage door.

After graduating from high school, both George and Elizabeth went on to study music at Mason College in Charleston, which is now part of Morris Harvey College. "Liz" majored in piano and to this day teaches that instrument. George majored in both piano and composition. They were married on May 21, 1949. While working their way through college, George was a pianist at a local ballet studio and the organist and choir director at a small Baptist church. He also helped his father with some music copying jobs.

In 1950, Crumb graduated with a Bachelor of Music degree. Also that year, his father died suddenly and the Crumbs' first child, Elizabeth Ann, was born.

George and his young family moved to Champaign-Urbana, where he began work on a masters degree in composition at the University of Illinois. George also began studying the viola. Like the clarinet, he later discontinued practicing it. However, he thinks that learning these instruments improved his ability to compose for string and woodwind instruments. One of his compositions written in 1952 was "Sonata," for viola and piano.

At this time, Crumb also became very interested in languages. He taught himself to read Spanish, German, French, and Italian. However, he never learned to speak a foreign language fluently. Crumb claims that the "musical ear" is much different than the "language ear."

After graduating with a Master of Music degree in 1952, Crumb moved his family to Ann Arbor, where he began a doctorate at the University of Michigan. There he studied composition with Ross Lee Finney, his most important teacher. Crumb also began his own teaching career, holding several teaching fellowships at the University of Michigan.

At the University of Michigan, Crumb heard his own compositions performed along with the works of other students. At one student concert, he heard the poetry of Federico García Lorca set to music. Crumb was deeply moved by the Spanish poet's vivid imagery. After reading more of García Lorca's poetry, he realized that what he wanted to express in music was similar to what the poet had conveyed in language. During the following two decades, Crumb used García Lorca's poetry in a cycle of eight large works.

In 1955, Crumb was awarded a Fulbright Fellowship to study music in Berlin. There he concentrated more on piano study than composition. He returned to Ann Arbor in 1957 to complete his doctorate.

Crumb continued to write many compositions, but none of them satisfied him very much. He wrote Sonata for Solo Violoncello in a style similar to Hungarian composer Béla Bartók and dedicated the work to his mother. For his thesis, he wrote *Variazioni* for orchestra, using the twelve-tone system and other techniques of Arnold Schönberg.

In 1958–59, Crumb taught music theory at Hollins College in Virginia. For the next five years he held a faculty position at the more prestigious University of Colorado at Boulder, where his teaching duties were somewhat disappointing. He taught the less talented piano students and was assigned only a few composition classes.

The Crumbs' second child, David Reed Crumb, was born in 1962. Also in that year, David Burge joined the piano faculty at the University of Colorado. He and Crumb shared an interest in new music and quickly became good friends. Burge asked Crumb if he would write some piano music for him. Crumb merely nodded and Burge decided that the composer wasn't that interested.

Actually, Crumb had started many compositions in the last three years, but had completed none. Nothing he wrote turned out to be what he actually wanted to express in music. About this time Crumb said, "I can remember quite literally waking up one night in a cold sweat with the realization that I had thus far simply been rewriting the music of other composers."

Crumb began thinking of ways in which he could make his compositions sound fresh and alive and like nothing that had ever been written before. He remembered Burge's request for music and decided to try out his new ideas in a group of piano pieces.

Crumb phoned Burge and asked him how he felt about playing inside the piano:

> Well, I thought it was a terrible idea," wrote Burge, "though I didn't say so. I also thought the very idea was rather insulting, but I didn't say that either. It occurred to me that, at the rate he [Crumb] moved, the piece would never get done anyway, so why worry? So I replied that, yes, it would be quite unusual to play inside the piano, that I had never done it, and that if he thought it necessary, I guessed I would learn how. I tried not to be overly encouraging.

Crumb then wrote *Five Pieces for Piano* (1962), in which he developed his own individual style. In this work he varies the quality of sound or timbre of the piano by requiring the performer to pluck the strings. The performer also lightly touches some strings while playing the coordinating keys. This produces high-pitched sounds called harmonics. Crumb requires the performer to use foreign objects such as paper clips to produce new sounds. He also explores new ways of using the three pedals.

Besides experimenting with timbre, Crumb worked

with very small units of sound, organizing a few pitches in unique rhythms. The number of beats or counts in each unit constantly changes throughout the piece. For example, Crumb used a group of two beats, followed by a group of seven, then three, then four, and so on.

When Crumb presented the *Five Pieces for Piano* to David Burge, the pianist was very puzzled. He had never seen a musical score that looked quite like it. He practiced the pieces for a month and gradually began to understand and appreciate them. He then performed them many times across the country.

The pieces were received with mixed reactions. Some listeners admired the pieces, others didn't like them, and some even laughed at them. Most listeners paid more attention to the unusual effect of playing inside the piano than to the craftsmanship of the music. Many listeners realized that they would have to hear *Five Pieces for Piano* more than once, perhaps many times, in order to appreciate them.

Crumb went on to compose in his new style for voice, percussion, and other instruments, using them in unusual combinations. Most of his pieces were chamber works, or pieces written for a small number of performers.

In 1964 Crumb received a Rockefeller grant, which gave him much more time to compose. He served as the "Composer-in-Residence" at the Buffalo Center for the Creative and Performing Arts in Buffalo, New York. He also performed as a pianist, playing new music of other composers. Crumb met many composers and performers in Buffalo. He liked the East Coast so much that he didn't want to move back to Colorado. In the spring of 1965, he was asked to join the composition faculty at the University of Pennsylvania, a post that he maintains today. Also in 1965, his third child, Peter Stanley Crumb, was born.

In the following year, soprano Jan DeGaetani premiered Crumb's *Madrigals, Books I and II* in Washington, D.C. This began a lifelong friendship and professional relationship between the composer and singer. When Crumb writes for soprano, he often has DeGaetani's voice in mind. "One of the deep satisfactions in working with Crumb," she wrote, "is the gift he gives you of knowing yourself more fully. He invents things that you've never done before and presents you with the need to leap into that unknown space and find a way to do them."

In 1968, Crumb was awarded the Pulitzer Prize in Music for his orchestral work, *Echoes of Time and the River.* Soon after, he composed *Songs, Drones, and Refrains of Death*, for baritone, electric guitar, electric contrabass, amplified piano, amplified harpsichord, and two percussionists. This was the first piece in which Crumb used electric instruments.

Crumb composed several more works, and then wrote *Black Angels* in 1970. This is a long work for electric string quartet. Crumb chose to electrically amplify the instruments to create a strange, other-worldly sound. Also, some of the special playing techniques are so soft that they would be difficult to hear without amplification.

According to the Bible, black angels were the follow-

George Crumb composing in his home while his son David plays with
"Tammy," in 1968
Used by permission from George Crumb

ers of the devil who battled against God and were cast into hell. A brief section of *Black Angels* is included in the score of *The Exorcist*, a movie about a girl possessed by the devil. *Black Angels* is divided into three parts: Departure, Absence, and Return. It represents a soul straying from God, existing under the influence of the devil and black angels, then returning to the grace of God.

Much of the music is eerie and haunting. Sudden loud accents jump out of the dark music and startle the listener. A highly rhythmic *Danse Macabre* in the second part represents ghouls dancing to a frenzy. Crumb quotes *Dies Irae*, a solemn medieval hymn about Judgment Day, which was often sung at funerals. Later in the piece, Crumb borrows compositional techniques of medieval music. The Middle Ages, also called the Dark Ages, was a time when people's thoughts were constantly on death, the end of the world, and the fear of spending eternity in hell.

Many of the rhythms used in *Black Angels* are based on the numbers seven and thirteen, which are both important in black magic and worship of the devil. On several occasions, the performers count in a ritualistic chant in several languages, including German, French, Russian, Hungarian, Japanese, and Swahili, to suggest the minutes of eternity ticking on and on.

At different times in the piece, the musicians play with thimble-capped fingers and use their bows on the wrong side of the strings, creating a scraping sound similar to the timbre of medieval instruments. Other special effects are created by maracas, Chinese gongs, and water-tuned crystal goblets stroked with the bow. The performers also slide their fingers lengthwise on the strings and use short rapid bowing on very high pitches to create the illusion of swarms of stinging insects.

Black Angels does not portray only evil, however. The music grows brighter and ligher in the "Return" section, representing the soul turning back to God. In this section, Crumb offers hope to our troubled modern world.

In 1970, Crumb composed *Ancient Voices of Children*, in which he used the poetry of Federico García Lorca. This piece is written for soprano, boy soprano, oboe, mandolin, harp, electric piano, toy piano, harmonica, a saw that is played with a bow, and many percussion instruments. One special sound effect is created by tuning one set of strings on the mandolin flat. Some of the other instruments are also required to "bend" pitches. The musicians play a note, then purposely go out of tune. The soprano sings vowels sounds which wildly rise and fall in pitch. She must shout, whisper, trill her tongue, and laugh. Sometimes she sings into the amplified piano, producing a shimmering echo.

About this piece Crumb wrote, "I have sought musical images that enhance and reinforce the powerful, yet strangely haunting imagery of Lorca's poetry. I feel that the essential meaning of this poetry is concerned with the most primary things: life, death, love, the smell of the earth, the sounds of the wind and the sea."

The work is divided into five songs with two instrumental interludes, "Dances of the Ancient Earth" and "Ghost Dance." The third song is subtitled "Dance of the Sacred Life-Cycle" and contains the rhythm of a Spanish dance called the bolero. In some concerts, a solo dancer performs these three sections.

Two of the songs are particularly interesting. In the third song, the boy soprano is off-stage so that he sounds lost and far away. The soprano and he half-sing, half-speak questions and answers to each other as if their separation causes them great pain.

The text of the fourth song is simply:

Each afternoon in Granada
a child dies each afternoon

Perhaps in this poem García Lorca is expressing the poverty, violence, and hardships of children during the Spanish Civil War. The poet himself was murdered during that war in 1936. In this fourth song, the toy piano plays a brief quotation taken from the little music book that J.S. Bach used to teach his children piano. The toy piano gradually plays slower—like a windup toy running down—symbolizing a child's death.

For his next major work, George Crumb was inspired by the singing of a humpback whale. The piece is called *Voice of the Whale* ("Vox Balaenae") (1971) and is written for three instruments: electric flute, electric cello, and amplified piano. The musicians who perform the work are required to wear black masks over the top part of their faces. The masks represent the impersonal forces of nature. Deep-blue stage lighting is used to suggest the ocean.

The sounds of the humpback whale are imitated by the flutist, who simultaneously plays the instrument and sings into it. The cellist produces the piercing cries of sea gulls by rapidly sliding her fingers down the strings, a technique called glissando. The pianist strums the lowest strings inside the instrument, which represents the deep, calm majesty of the sea.

The concluding section of *Voice of the Whale* is called "Sea Nocturne (. . . for the end of time)". "In composing the Sea Nocturne," wrote Crumb, "I wanted to suggest a larger rhythm of nature and a sense of suspension in time." When listening to this section of the piece, you may imagine how humpback whales sense time—certainly not in minutes, hours, months, and years as we humans do.

Voice of the Whale ends with many repetitions of a ten-note figure. The figure grows softer and softer, finally dying away to silence. The performers pantomime the last playing of the figure, as if the music goes on beyond the range of human ears and continues to sound throughout nature.

Though Crumb composed rapidly in his youth, he now works very slowly and painstakingly, composing about one major work a year, including *Makrokosmos, Vol I* (1972) and *II*, (1973) for solo piano; *Star Child*, (1977) for soprano, children's voices, and orchestra; *A Haunted Landscape*, (1984) for orchestra; and *The Sleeper* (1984) for soprano and piano.

About his work habits, Crumb has said, "My daily schedule is quite variable: sometimes an hour or two of work will completely exhaust me, while at other times

I can sustain my concentration over many hours. Generally, once I fully understand the implications of my materials, the work sessions tend to become longer."

George Crumb continues to teach at the University of Pennsylvania. He and Liz live in Media, a small town near Philadelphia. Their children are all grown. Crumb continued making fireworks for his children every Fourth of July for many years. Oddly, instead of improving his technique, he produced more and more duds. As his explosions got smaller and his clouds of black smoke grew bigger, his children lost interest and his wife stopped worrying. Finally Crumb gave up pyrotechnics completely. He now likes quieter activi-

Crumb offers advice to the Penn Contemporary Players while they rehearse his music, 1975
Used by permission from George Crumb

ties such as reading books on astronomy, archaeology, and history, as well as Sherlock Holmes and mystery novels. He also enjoys playing chamber music and piano duets with his friends.

George Crumb has won many honors and has been praised by many critics, yet he remains modest. "I am delighted when my music is played and understood," said Crumb. "However, I have not yet written a piece that totally satisfies me. [It was] once said that to have written only two or three truly superb pages of music would justify one's being a composer. I would one day like to write those two or three pages."

Steve Reich
Martha Swope Assocs/Linda Alaniz

Chapter Nine
STEVE REICH
(1936-   )

Have you ever heard the expression "Less is more"? It sounds almost like a riddle; yet the concept is easy to understand. Suppose you were treated to a feast of your favorite foods and you ate and ate until you felt sick. You would discover that eating less is more satisfying. Or suppose you shot a photograph that included so many great things that it looked cluttered. You would realize that including less is more pleasing to your eye.

"Less is more" is the premise of minimalism. There are minimalist movements in art, literature, and music. In minimalist music there is less melody and less harmony. The rhythm is vibrant and insistently pulsing like the beat in rock music. Small fragments of melody or a few chords are repeated over and over. This has led some people to call it "trance music," "hypnotic music," even "stuck-in-the-groove music." Changes are made over a long period of time so that the ending of a piece is usually quite different from the beginning but these changes are so gradual that a listener might be surprised that so much progress has been made.

Listening to a piece of minimalist music may be much like taking a long car trip when you were little. You ride and ride for a very long, long time, gazing out the window at the landscape, which changes ever so gradually: flat to hilly, green to brown, no houses to more houses, and then suddenly the car stops. You've reached your destination without actually knowing how you got there, and in that moment of arrival you feel a sense of accomplishment, surprise, and delight.

The "father" of minimalist music is La Monte Young, who was inspired by raga music of India. Young influenced composer Terry Riley, who wrote his most well-known piece, *In C*, in 1964. *In C*, which can be played by any combination of instruments, consists of fifty-three short melodies or motives. Each performer plays and repeats each motive as many times as he wishes. The piece ends when every performer has played through all fifty-three fragments. One musician who played in *In C* was Steve Reich. He was a composer as well as a performer and went on to apply some of Riley's techniques to his own writing.

Stephen Michael Reich was born October 3, 1936, in New York City. His mother was pop singer and lyricist June Sillman, who wrote the song "Love is a

Simple Thing." His father was Leonard Reich, an attorney. Steve's parents were divorced soon after he was born, and he spent his first five years going back and forth between his mother in Beverly Hills and his father in Manhattan. Steve's earliest musical memory is of dancing around at bedtime at age three while his maternal grandfather, Mort Sillman, played the piano.

At age five, Steve moved in permanently with his father. He grew up in a Jewish neighborhood in the upper West side of Manhattan and was brought up in the Reform Jewish faith. Steve was a great fan of the New York Yankees and often played baseball in the street with his friends. One of his great thrills as a boy was seeing Babe Ruth, then retired, driving his big black Cadillac through the neighborhood. Ruth would stick his head out of the window and say, "Hello boys," his voice gravelly from throat cancer.

Later, Steve's father moved his family to the suburbs in Larchmont, New York. Steve studied piano three years, but the simplified classical and romantic music he was given didn't hold his interest. When he was fourteen, a neighbor, who owned a large record collection, invited him to listen to Stravinsky's *Rite of Spring* and Bach's *Brandenburg* concertos. Steve found these works to be a lot more impressive than the music he had played on the piano. Stravinsky and Bach would later have a major influence on his own composition.

Steve also listened to bebop jazz artists Charlie Parker, Miles Davis, and Kenny Clarke. "I loved the way Kenny Clarke played drums," recalls Reich. "I had a friend who was a pianist and we wanted to form a band, so I was elected drummer instantly." Steve then began studying drums with Roland Kohloff.

Enrolled in an accelerated program at school, Steve skipped third grade and graduated from high school a year early. At age sixteen he entered Cornell University, where he majored in philosophy and played drums on the weekends. He also enrolled in music classes, some taught by William Austin. Steve dreamed of being a composer, but remembers thinking, "Mozart was five when he started composing, Bartók was six. I was seventeen, so I was wondering if it was too late for me." Professor Austin, however, encouraged him to compose. After graduating with a degree in philosophy in 1957, Reich moved to New York City. There he studied composition privately for two years with Hall Overton, a composer and jazz musician who was a friend of jazz great Thelonious Monk.

Reich then entered the Juilliard School of Music as a sophomore and completed his second bachelor's degree. For his graduate work in music, he attended Mills College in Oakland, California, where he studied with composers Darius Milhaud and Luciano Berio. He received his M.A. in 1963.

Throughout his academic years, Reich felt somewhat ill at ease. At Juilliard he had kept a low profile as a drummer because he thought, "Classical composers aren't bebop drummers." Also, all the composition professors of the 1950s and 1960s taught serialism, a style of music that Reich had no interest in. (For an explanation of serialism, see page 142.)

So instead of hanging out with the composition

students at Mills, Reich got a job at Yellow Cab. He also took other menial jobs until about 1971, when he was able to support himself by playing his own music. "I wanted mindless work," says Reich, "so making a living would have no determination on my music. Actually, it didn't work out that way. I bugged my cab. I wrote a piece called *Livelihood,* a tape collage of sounds in a taxicab."

After completing his study at Mills, Reich stayed around the San Francisco Bay Area for a couple more years. It was at this time that he became involved with playing in Terry Riley's *In* C.

Reich moved back to New York in 1965 and began to experiment with electronic music. He created tape pieces by recording sounds on bits of tape and splicing them together. A civil rights activist named Truman Nelson heard that Reich worked with tape recorders. Nelson was putting on a benefit to raise money for the appeal hearing of the "Harlem Six," six black youths convicted for the murder of a white woman. Nelson asked Reich to edit ten hours of court transcripts to be played at the benefit. This was a very strange request to make of a composer since it had nothing to do with music. Reich told Nelson that he usually didn't do that kind of work, but he would be willing to if he were allowed to use part of the transcript to make a piece.

The result was the tape piece *Come Out.* From the entire ten hours of talking, Reich chose to use only five words taken from the testimony of a convicted black teenager. While speaking about police brutality, the youth said, "I had to, like, open the bruise up and let some of the bruise blood come out to show them."

At the beginning of *Come Out*, two copies of the phrase "Come out to show them" are heard simultaneously and repeated many times. Gradually one tape speeds up and gets slightly ahead of the other so that the two are out of sync. In this way, Reich uses electronic manipulations to intensify the rhythms of American street talk. *Come Out* gives a listener time to appreciate the acoustic richness of speech patterns. The piece could also serve as a sort of motto, capsulizing the entire civil rights movement.

Also in 1966, Reich formed an ensemble called Steve Reich and Musicians, which still performs his works today. The group started with three musicians, including Reich, playing percussion and piano. Today the group includes up to thirty pianists, marimba/xylophonists, clarinetists, violinists, cellists, and vocalists. Between 1971 and 1985 Steve Reich and Musicians completed sixteen European and American tours, playing more than three hundred concerts.

Steve Reich and Musicians received their first major hearing in 1967 at a minimalist art show in a Soho gallery. Following that, Reich played many more concerts in art museums. "In the early days," says Reich, "I was getting more support from the world of painting and sculpture than from the world of classical music." Reich and Musicians have also appeared at the Whitney Museum, the Guggenheim Museum, and the Museum of Modern Art in New York, the University Art

Museum in Berkeley, the Boston Museum of Fine Art, and others.

Reich continued to be interested in the idea of two identical fragments of sound gradually growing "out of phase" or "out of sync" with one another. In his book *Writings About Music* he states:

> I had the idea that if a number of single tones were all pulsing at the same tempo, but with gradually shifting phase relations, a great number of musical patterns would result. If the tones were all in phase (struck at the same instant), a pulsing chord would be heard. If the tones were slowly shifted just a bit out of phase, a sort of rippling broken chord would be heard which would gradually change into a melodic pattern, then another, and so on. If the process of phase shifting were gradual enough, then minute rhythmic difference would become clearly audible. A given musical pattern would then be heard to change into another with no alteration of pitch, timbre, or loudness, and one would become involved in a music which worked exclusively with gradual changes in time.

Reich was certain that such rhythmically precise music would be impossible for humans to play. He thought he would have to rely on electronics as a means of realizing his music. In February of 1968, Reich presented his ideas to Larry Owens, an electronic engineer at the Bell Laboratories in Holmdel, New Jersey. What resulted was the invention of a device Reich called the Phase Shifting Pulse Gate.

In April and May of 1969, Reich performed his work *Pulse Music* on the Phase Shifting Pulse Gate at The New School in New York and at the Whitney Museum of American Art. The Phase Shifting Pulse Gate was able to produce the musical effects Reich was seeking but he found the performance of the electronic device to be stiff and unmusical. He realized that the tiny variations of a steady pulse created by human beings playing musical instruments and singing was what breathed life into music. Besides, twisting dials on a machine was not nearly as fun as playing a musical instrument. Reich began to think of possible ways that live musicians could play his phase-shifting music.

In January of 1970, Reich completed a piece he named *Four Organs*. He describes the work simply as "short chord gets long." Four organists play a single six-note chord throughout the entire twenty-five minutes of the piece. The chord is played in very short durations to start with, then gradually gets longer. A maracas player shakes out steady eighth-notes throughout the work. The organists stay together by counting the eighth-note beats, sometimes as many as two hundred in one group of sustained notes.

In *Four Organs* there is no change in timbre or pitch. All changes are rhythmic. It would seem then that there is not much to listen to; however, that isn't true. Rather, you would have to do a different kind of listening than you are used to. You might call it listening in slow motion. Think how many different chords you would hear in a twenty-five minute Beethoven symphony. Yet they go by so fast, you don't get much of a chance to really hear them individually. You would be more concerned with how the chords relate to each other in what is called harmonic progression.

Listening to *Four Organs* is like looking at a leaf

under a microscope. You might not think there's much to see in a tiny leaf, but if you look at it magnified a hundred times you will perhaps see evidence of the entire life-cycle of an insect. In listening to a single chord for twenty-five minutes you will also hear details in music that you have never heard before. *Four Organs* gives you time to really hear how individual notes relate to others in a chord. Some of the tones are slightly out of phase with others, creating a kind of rippling melody. Some tones are held longer than others at various times in the piece so that you hear relationships between different combinations of tones. As you listen to *Four Organs* you would also become very aware of overtones. Every pitch has a series of natural overtones. When a pitch is sounded, its related overtones are faintly heard. We are not so aware of overtones when we have to listen "fast."

All of these aspects have to do with pitch and are actually of secondary importance. The most vital thing about *Four Organs* is the rhythm. The relentless maracas hurl us forward in time. As the chord lengthens, the tension grows. The piece becomes more and more exciting as it moves along.

Unfortunately, however, this type of listening does not have a positive effect on everyone. When *Four Organs* was performed by members of the Boston Symphony Orchestra, a riot almost broke out. Some listeners yelled for the music to stop and others shouted for it to keep going. The audience grew so loud that the performers could not hear each other. Conductor Michael Tilson Thomas had to mouth the counts to keep the group together. One woman jumped from her seat, ran down the aisle, and pounded on the stage. "I can't stand it any longer!" she shouted at the startled musicians. After the performance, Thomas remarked to Reich, "This is it. This is fantastic! You've finally gotten under their skin."

This, of course, was not the only time in history that listeners took it personally when musicians played music they didn't like. Debussy, Stravinsky, Cowell, and other composers have experienced violent reactions to their music.

After drumming on organs, Reich was eager to get back to drumming on drums. Much of his music contains an emphasis on percussion because his interest in music began with playing the drums. By 1970 he knew a lot about rudimental snare drumming and jazz drumming. He had also studied African drumming in a book by A. M. Jones. To reinforce what he had learned from Jones, Reich attended the Institute for African Studies at the University of Ghana in Accra. There he underwent a different kind of learning experience than those he had encountered in the United States. Instead of reading music, he had to rely on his memory in order to imitate the complex drumming techniques of the African instructors.

Much of African drumming is based on a meter or group of twelve beats. When African drummers play together, one will divide the twelve beats into groups of four, another will play in groups of three, and still another in groups of two. In other words, one drummer might count: 1 2 3 4   1 2 3 4   1 2 3 4; another would count: 1 2 3   1 2 3   1 2 3   1 2 3; and another would think: 1 2   1 2   1 2   1 2   1 2   1 2. These different groupings are then layered one on top of the other, creating cross rhythms.

That's not all there is to African drumming. The most interesting aspect is that each drummer plays the first beat, or downbeat, at a different time. With so many players going on at once it is difficult to tell who has the downbeat when. This concept is very different from music in our Western culture in which the down-beat is very strong and obvious. You can easily find the downbeat in most rock music by tapping the pulse and counting in groups of four. The strong pulse you feel every fourth beat is the downbeat.

Reich is very interested in this idea of making the downbeat hard to find or ambiguous. "That's the magic of African drumming," he says, "and the difficulty." Since musicians who play Western music are used to staying together by playing the downbeat simultane-ously, they find Reich's music very challenging.

After returning from Africa, Reich took more than a year to compose and rehearse *Drumming*, a work that lasts about an hour and a half. *Drumming* is divided into four sections, which are played one after another without pauses. The first section is for eight small tuned drums and male voices; the second section is for three marimbas and female voices; the third section is for three glockenspiels, whistling, and a piccolo; and, in the last section, all the instruments and voices are combined. The vocalists sing syllables such as "tuk," "tok," and "duk" to imitate the sounds of the instruments. They also sing melodic patterns that result from the instruments playing out of phase with each other.

Steve Reich in his New York studio, 1971
Used by permission from Keyboard Magazine

After composing *Drumming*, Reich studied Balinese gamelan under the direction of Balinese teachers at the American Society for Eastern Arts in Seattle and Berkeley. Gamelan is a type of orchestra from southeast Asia that includes combinations of drums, gongs, cymbals, and wind and stringed instruments. Tuning systems are based on five-note and seven-notes scales that differ from the major and minor scales that we use in Western music. Balinese music is characterized by animated drumming and short, rapid melodies that repeat over and over.

In 1971, when Steve Reich and Musicians were touring with *Drumming* in Europe, Reich happened to visit a flamenco club in Brussels. He was impressed by how much music the performers made merely by clapping. At the time, Reich and his group were lugging around thousands of pounds of instruments and sound equipment. He was understandably intrigued with the idea of composing music simply for two pairs of hands. This inspired the piece *Clapping Music*.

Clapping Music is another one of Reich's "phase" pieces. It is very difficult for one performer to get gradually ahead of the other by merely clapping, so instead the second performer jumps ahead one beat each time a shift occurs. *Clapping Music* is divided into thirteen sections of twelve beats and each section is repeated twelve times. The first performer remains fixed, clapping the same twelve-beat rhythmic pattern throughout. The second performer starts the rhythmic pattern in unison with the first performer, then shifts the downbeat over one beat at the beginning of each new section. For example, beats 1 2 3 4 5 6 7 8 9 10 11 12 in the first section are played 2 3 4 5 6 7 8 9 10 11 12 1 in the second section, 3 4 5 6 7 8 9 10 11 12 1 2 in the third section, and so on. This change in downbeat makes it difficult to hear that the second performer is actually playing the same rhythmic pattern as the first performer in each section of the piece. Anyone who understands eighth notes and eighth rests is theoretically capable of playing *Clapping Music*, but it requires lots of concentration!

For a long time Reich had wanted to write a composition for all the pianos in a piano store. In 1973, the Baldwin Piano and Organ Company gave him permis-

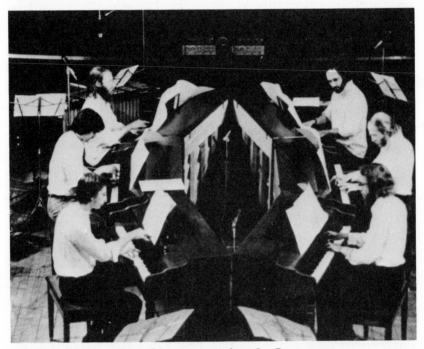

Steve Reich (upper right) and Musicians perform Six Pianos
Used by permission from Keyboard Magazine

sion to hold rehearsals in their New York store in the evenings after closing time. Reich soon discovered that all those pianos were just too much to work with. Pianos, especially grand pianos, have so many loud overtones that when the musicians tried to play too many of them at once, nothing much could be heard but a lot of loud, fuzzy sound. Reich settled for six spinet pianos pushed close together so the musicians could hear each other. Using the pianos like a series of tuned drums, Reich composed the piece *Six Pianos*. The piano is, afterall, a percussion instrument—the sound is produced by hammers striking strings.

Other important works that Reich composed were Music for Mallet Instruments, Voices, and Organ in 1973 and Music for 18 Musicians in 1974. Jerome Robbins choreographed Reich's *Eight Lines* for the New York City Ballet, which premiered in 1985. Laura Dean choreographed *Sextet* for her dance "Impact." It premiered during the 1985 NEXT WAVE Festival and both Reich and Dean won a Bessie Award for it in 1986.

Over the years, many symphony orchestras and concert artists have asked Reich to write pieces for them to play. Flutist Ransom Wilson asked Reich to write a concerto for him. Reich doesn't like the idea of a concerto—one solo instrument pitted against an entire orchestra. He much prefers to write music in which the musicians have fairly equal parts. However, he didn't want to turn down Wilson so he came up with *Vermont Counterpoint*.

This piece is for solo flute and is accompanied by a tape recording. On the recording is the same flutist playing ten other parts on flute, alto flute, and piccolo. It is especially challenging for the flutist to record ten perfect ten-minute tracks. One mistake and he or she has to begin again. Reich also wrote two similar pieces: *New York Counterpoint* in 1985 for clarinetist Richard Stoltzman, and *Electric Counterpoint* in 1987 for guitarist Pat Metheny.

In 1982 Steve Reich departed from his previous techniques to write one of his major works, *Tehillim*. In it he used the same compositional devices as J.S. Bach and other European composers. *Tehillim* is rich in timbre, melody, and emotion. Many people think it is the most joyous of all of Reich's works.

In preparation for composing *Tehillim*, Reich returned to his Jewish roots. About being brought up Reform Jewish he claims, "I got absolutely no information. I had a lip-sync bar mitzvah. I pointed to squiggles. I knew not what they meant, and cared not." At age thirty-seven Reich began to care very much. He studied the Torah and the traditional chanting of the Hebrew Scriptures with rabbis and scholars in New York and Jerusalem.

Tehillim, which means "Praises," consists of four psalms in Hebrew text set to music. Originally *Tehillim* was played by Steve Reich and Musicians, but later the composer arranged the work for full orchestra.

In the work, Reich uses a tambourine without jingles that is similar to a small drum called a *tof* in Hebrew. He also has written for hand clapping and rattles (maracas), both of which were often used throughout the Middle East during Biblical times. The vocalists use a non-operatic style of singing. The lack of heavy vibrato gives the singing a pure, natural sound much like the tone quality of an accomplished folk singer.

For *Tehillim*, Reich set text for the first time since college. The rhythm of the piece follows the rhythm of the Hebrew language, causing the meter to constantly change throughout the piece. Reich didn't use the short melodic repeated patterns that appear in his earlier pieces because he wanted to set the text according to its own rhythm and meaning.

However, repetition of melodic ideas and rhythm are heard throughout *Tehillim*. That is because Reich uses a compositional device called imitative counterpoint. "Counterpoint" means "point against point." Notes were once called points. In other words, counterpoint is two or more melodies played simultaneously. In imitative counterpoint a melody is introduced in one part or voice and the other voices follow the first, using similar material. A canon is the strictest form of imitative counterpoint. In a canon, the voices sing the exact same melody, but start it at different times. You probably have had some first-hand experience with canons through singing a round such as "Row, Row, Row Your Boat." In a way, Reich's phase pieces are like canons, with the imitative voices coming in very close together.

The first text of *Tehillim* begins as a solo with drum and clapping accompaniment. Four vocalists, doubled by the instruments, sing four four-part canons on each of the four verses of the text. A solo voice then restates the original melody with drum and string accompaniment. The second text begins immediately after a short drum transition. Here the melody lines grow longer and longer and become more ornate. After a pause the third text begins in a slow tempo with marimba and vibraphone accompaniment. (It is interesting to note that this is the first slow music Reich had composed since his student days.) The fourth text returns to the original tempo and consists of materials taken from all three movements. The words are quite appropriate for a musical setting:

> *Praise Him with drum and dance,*
> *praise Him with strings and winds.*
> *praise Him with sounding cymbals.*
> *praise Him with clanging cymbals.*
> *Let all that breathes praise the Eternal*
> *Hallelujah.*

The coda or last section of the movement is based on the single word "Hallelujah." It may remind some listeners that Handel, who lived in the Baroque era like Bach, composed "The Hallelujah Chorus" based on that one word. *Tehillim* grows louder and louder and ends with an ecstatic sound of all voices and instruments clamoring together.

In 1982–83, Reich wrote *The Desert Music.* This was his first work conceived originally for orchestra and chorus. In it, Reich uses compositional devices he has used before, but he reaches far beyond his minimalist beginnings, both in material and range of emotion. Two of Reich's influences are most obvious: the driving, accented rhythms of Stravinsky's *Rite of Spring* and the dissonant jazz harmonies of Thelonius Monk. The name *The Desert Music* is taken from a book of verse by American poet William Carlos Williams. For the text, Reich chose excerpts from Williams's poem "The Orchestra" and other works.

While Reich was composing *Desert Music* in a small town in Vermont, the local fire siren went off. Right then, he decided to put a siren in the music. Instead of using a mechanical one, Reich has the violas, equipped with contact mikes, play glissandos that rise and fall over the entire orchestra and chorus.

Reich composed one more large orchestra work, *The Four Sections*, which was premiered by the San Francisco Symphony in November 1987. He then returned to the use of tape and smaller ensembles.

Reich composed *Different Trains* in 1988 for the Kronos Quartet, a string quartet renown for their vibrant interpretations of new music. In the work, Kronos plays against three separate recordings of themselves that are combined with speech and train sounds. The concept of the work stems from Reich's early interest in speech melody reflected in his taped speech piece *Come Out*. The subject matter is taken from Reich's very early childhood when his parents had divided custody of him. In the program notes he wrote:

> *I traveled back and forth by train frequently between New York and Los Angeles from 1939 to 1942 accompanied by my governess. While these trips were exciting and romantic at the time, I now look back and think that, if I had been in Europe during this period, as a Jew I would have had to ride very different trains.*

These "different trains" that Reich is referring to were cattle cars packed with Jews riding toward torture and death in the concentration camps of Nazi Germany.

To prepare the tape for *Different Trains*, Reich recorded the voice of his governess, a Pullman porter who used to ride lines between New York and Los Angeles in the forties, and survivors of the Holocaust. From this material, the composer selected short phrases such as: "from Chicago to New York," "they tatooed a number on our arm," and "going to America." He then notated the speech melodies and used them as the music that the string quartet imitates.

Different Trains for which Reich won a Grammy in 1990, is therefore both a piece of music and a documentary. For his next major work, Reich plans to extend this idea by adding documentary video tape projected on large screens to the live and taped music, voices, and sounds. He calls this new art form "documentary music video theater." In effect, it will be Reich's own unique way of composing "opera."

Steve Reich now lives in New York City with his wife, video artist Beryl Korot, and their eleven-year-old son, Ezra. Korot works in the mediums of four-channel video (a type of film-making using video cameras) and painting on hand-woven canvas. She will be collaborating with Reich on the new theater work. Reich also has a twenty-seven-year-old son, Michael, from a previous marriage.

As for his work habits, Reich composes at the piano. He uses pencil because he says he is always willing to change something. Recently he began using a computer to generate printed scores and parts. While he is working on a piece he often pauses to try things out on the instruments he plays. Sometimes he tapes some parts and plays against them; other times he asks other musicians to try parts with him. When he is not touring with Steve Reich and Musicians he keeps regular hours, composing from ten A.M. to six P.M. He tries to devote his evenings to his family and observes the Sabbath by not composing Friday nights and Saturdays.

Reich's advice to kids who want to be composers is to play and study music. "Studying four-part harmony and counterpoint may bore you at times," he says, "but don't fool yourselves. As you get older you will use these skills in unforeseen ways. The more you learn, the farther you can go."

He also suggests, "At a time when no one knows or cares much about you, get together with your friends and play your own music. If you're a keyboard player, do that; if you're a conductor, do that; if you're a synthesizer programmer, do that; whatever. Get involved with the performance of your own music, and then at least we'll really know what you've got in mind."

Philip Glass
Martha Swope Assoc/Rebecca Lesher; used by permission from IPA/International Production
Associates, Inc

Chapter Ten
PHILIP GLASS
(1937–   )

◆

You may know some music by Philip Glass without realizing it. Maybe you heard it on "Sesame Street" when you were a little kid or, more recently, on "Saturday Night Live." Philip Glass's music was played at the opening and closing ceremonies of the 1984 Summer Olympics in Los Angeles. He also wrote the film scores for the movies *Mishima* and *A Thin Blue Line*.

Like Steve Reich, Philip Glass is considered to be part of the minimalist movement. (See page 171 for an explanation of minimalism.) The composers knew each other when they were both students at the Juilliard School of Music. They met again ten years later

193

at a concert Steve Reich and Musicians played at a minimalist art show in a Soho gallery. The composers talked a lot about music and shared similar views. They also played in each other's ensembles. As a result some people lump their work together, mentioning both composers in one breath. Reich and Glass, however, have taken separate paths in composition, and their work sounds very different from one another.

Philip was born January 31, 1937, in Baltimore, Maryland, the youngest of three children. His sister, Sheppie, is two years older and his brother, Martin, is one year older. None of the other Glass family members were musicians. However, Philip's father owned a record store that sold all kinds of music. Mr. Glass's favorite music was classical string quartets and piano and cello sonatas. Philip's first musical experience was listening to recordings of this kind of music with his father.

When Philip was six years old, he took violin lessons with the rest of his grammar school class. At eight, he attended the Peabody Conservatory where he began his study of flute, percussion, and music theory. By then, he already knew that he wanted to be a musician.

While growing up during World War II, Philip was interested in science, especially astronomy. He built a telescope with the help of some adult amateur astronomers. One of Philip's heroes was Einstein, whose theory of relativity marked the beginning of the nuclear age. Stories and photographs about the famous physicist were often in the news. Philip read many books about him, including ones that Einstein himself wrote. This information all came in handy twenty-five years later when Philip decided to write an opera about Einstein.

As a teenager, Philip had a wide range of interests. During junior high, he played quarterback with a neighborhood football club. When he was twelve, he worked in his father's record store. He was also one of the youngest members of the Maryland Chess Club.

At age fifteen, Philip entered the University of Chicago. Soon after, he wrote his first composition, a twelve-tone piece for string trio. (For an explanation of twelve-tone music, see page 142.) A year later, Philip rejected twelve-tone. He wasn't sure what his composing style would be, but he knew he wanted to write tonal music using traditional keys and chords in new ways. Also during college, Philip took up the piano and practiced regularly for several years.

Philip graduated with a Bachelor's of Music in 1956 and began his graduate studies at the Juilliard School of Music, where he studied with composers Vincent Persichetti and William Bergsma. During the next five years Philip wrote over seventy compositions, including string quartets, concertos, and choral music. Many of these works were performed in concerts, and twenty or more were published by Elkan-Vogel Music Publishers. These were all good student compositions, but Glass had not yet discovered his own unique style.

While at Juilliard, Glass continued his piano study, but only when he could steal time from his composing. Composition majors didn't usually practice an instrument because they were never expected to play their own music. Performance majors, who practiced six or more hours a day, could do a much better job.

After graduating with a Master of Music degree, Philip received a Ford Foundation Fellowship that enabled him to work as a composer-in-residence in Pittsburgh. His job was to write pieces for public school and community bands and orchestras to play.

Philip then received a Fulbright Scholarship, which allowed him to travel to Paris to study with Nadia Boulanger. During her long teaching career Boulanger attracted many international students, including American composers Elliott Carter and Aaron Copland.

> Glass recalls that "For Boulanger, my Juilliard achievements didn't count at all. I remember the first afternoon I spent with her at her apartment/studio on the Rue Ballou. She was seventy-seven at the time, a tough, aristocratic Frenchwoman elegantly dressed in fashions fifty years out of date. In dead silence, she read through pages and pages of the music I had brought her. I think I must have been quite proud of some of it. Finally, after an eternity of silent perusal, she pounced on a measure, pointed triumphantly at it, and declared: 'There. This was written by a real composer.' That was the first and last time she said anything nice to me for the next two years."

Boulanger believed in getting back to the basics. Her rigorous training included counterpoint, harmony, analysis of music, and ear training exercises. Philip began to hear things in music he had previously overlooked. He learned to concentrate and apply his talents in such a way that he could accomplish more than he ever expected.

Although Glass acquired much in discipline and musical skills, he still had not gotten any closer to developing his own style. Then one day he got an unexpected opportunity. He learned from a friend that the renowned Indian sitar player, Ravi Shankar, was in Paris writing music for a film score. The music system of India is very different from Western music. Shankar needed someone to listen to his music, then transcribe it in Western notation so that the French musicians could read it. Glass eagerly took on the job, even though he knew nothing about Indian music.

Glass spent the next several months with Ravi Shankar and his drummer, Alla Rakha. He learned that rhythm was organized quite differently in Indian music. In Western music, measures of music are divided into smaller units. In Indian music, small units or "beats" are strung together to make larger time values.

Shankar composed a piece for small orchestra by singing each instrumental part straight through, one at a time. Glass had no trouble notating the pitches that Shankar sang since that was like the ear training exercises Boulanger assigned him. Glass's problem was figuring out how to notate the Indian rhythms. At first, he divided the beats into measures. This caused the musicians to play accents like the way they played Western music. Alla Rakha told Glass the music sounded wrong. It was all supposed to flow without accents.

Glass tried taking all the measure lines out of the music. It worked! The notes all sounded equal. This was a powerful concept for Glass. He began to think about rhythm in a whole new way. He applied these ideas to his own compositions. His music sounds nothing like Indian music, but his experience with Shankar had a great influence on him. He was beginning to see what kind of music he really wanted to write.

Glass then had to find an audience for his ideas. The only new music event in Paris was the "Domain Musicale" concert series, organized by composer-conductor Pierre Boulez. Boulez was only interested in programming twelve-tone music, a technique that Glass had rejected as a teenager. Glass felt that serialism belonged to an earlier generation of composers and that it was time to explore new methods of composition.

Since Glass could not find a nitch in the musical circles of Paris, he turned to the theater. He found that many actors and directors were involved with staging experimental productions. Their work didn't tell a story that had a beginning, middle, and end like traditional plays. Instead, they presented material in a way that could alter the viewers' normal way of thinking. The audience members were inspired to examine their values, sense of order, and views of society.

Glass met an experimental theater group who later called themselves the Mabou Mines. One member was JoAnne Akalaitis, whom Glass later married. The group needed a composer to write incidental music for their productions. Glass was elected. Over the next twenty years he wrote at least a dozen scores for the company.

For the Mabou Mine production *Play*, Glass wrote a piece for two soprano saxophonists who each played only two notes. When the saxophone parts were combined, the pitches remained static, but the shifting patterns of rhythms pulsed with variety.

Glass's music was met with opposition. The French musicians didn't want to play a piece with only four notes. The French audiences didn't want to hear it. The Mabou Mines players had problems, too. There was not a large enough English-speaking audience in Paris to support their efforts. In 1967, Glass and the Mabou Mines decided to try their luck in New York City.

The late 1960s and early 1970s was an exciting time for artists to live in New York. Actors, directors, musicians, painters, sculptors, filmmakers, poets, and writers formed their own community in a part of Manhattan South of Houston Street, nicknamed "Soho." The experimental theater that was presented in Soho was called "Off-Off-Broadway." The players didn't make much money and had difficulty financing their productions. Most of the performing artists took menial jobs in copy shops and restaurants to support themselves. Glass worked as a plumber and cab driver. The jobs were no fun and took time away from his composing, but at least he was able to write the kind of music he wanted and hear it performed.

Besides his theater pieces, Glass composed other music. Instead of depending on other musicians to perform his work, he formed the Philip Glass Ensemble. Glass played the piano and so did two of his friends. It was awkward to get three pianos together, so Glass decided to use electric organs, which he later

Philip Glass Ensemble performing at the Peppermint Lounge, 1980
Used by permission from Keyboard Magazine

replaced with synthesizers. Also included in the ensemble were three wind players, who doubled on saxophone, flute, and bass clarinet, and a soprano, who sang wordless texts. Because of the electric keyboards, Glass knew the whole group had to be amplified. He hired a sound designer/mixer to join the group.

The group first recorded *Music with Changing Parts*, a ninety minute piece, on Glass's own label, Chatham Square Productions. To finance the project, Glass borrowed five hundred dollars from the Hebrew Free Loan Association, a fund to help newly arrived immigrants get their own businesses started in America. Glass didn't exactly qualify, but they gave him the loan anyway.

The Philip Glass Ensemble started performing in the same places as the theater groups. Often they gave concerts in Soho artists' lofts and art galleries. In 1971 they went on their first European tour. Today they perform all over the world.

The Philip Glass Ensemble has at least three things in common with rock groups. They use electric instruments, they have popular appeal, and they're LOUD. Once when the ensemble appeared at Louise Davies Symphony Hall, the San Francisco Symphony season ticket holders in the audience were shocked by the deafening decibels. In the moment of silence between the last reverberating notes and the beginning of the applause, one symphony goer with a sense of humor shouted, "Louder!"

Between 1971 and 1974, Glass organized his ideas about rhythm into one large work called *Music in Twelve Parts*. In the work there are few changes in melody and harmony. Gradual rhythmic changes are extended over a five-hour period.

Glass never planned to be an opera composer, but that is what he turned out to be. It is not so surprising, considering all his work in theater. For his first opera, he collaborated with Robert Wilson, an important figure in experimental theater. Glass and Wilson began their work by merely meeting for lunch almost every Thursday for a year to get to know each other and discuss ideas. They soon agreed that Albert Einstein would be their subject. Wilson thought up the title "Einstein on the Beach on Wall Street," which was later shortened to *Einstein on the Beach*.

Neither Glass nor Wilson were interested in producing a traditional play that would tell the story of Einstein's life. Instead, they planned to present images and sound that would mean something different to each member of the audience, depending on his or her imagination and knowledge of Einstein.

Wilson drew sketches of suggested scenes in storyboards or visual workbooks. From these, he and Glass chose a nineteenth century train, a court room, and a spaceship to be the most important scenes in their opera.

The cast for *Einstein on the Beach* consists of four main characters: two women, a young boy, and an old man. A sixteen-member chorus sings with non-operatic voices and the orchestra is the Philip Glass Ensemble. Since Einstein was an amateur violinist, a violinist plays the character Einstein.

The length of the opera is close to five hours. Some of the scenes are acted out so slowly that they seem almost frozen in time. Two fast dance sections change the pace of the action.

The production includes many interesting details. A bar of light represents a bed. The chorus members are all dressed in an Einstein costume of baggy pants, suspenders, and short-sleeved shirts. All the furniture used on stage is made out of plumbing pipes, since Einstein had once said that if he had his life to live over again he would have been a plumber. The final scene takes place inside the spaceship in which a three-level grid of cubicles holds all the performers, including members of the Philip Glass Ensemble.

Much of the spoken text for *Einstein on the Beach* was written by Christopher Knowles, a fourteen-year-old mentally-disturbed poet. Other texts were developed by two of the actors, Samuel M. Johnson and Lucinda Childs, during rehearsals.

Glass began writing the music for *Einstein on the Beach* in the spring of 1975 and completed it in November. He didn't want to set text to music, yet the chorus members needed something to help them remember their part. He decided to use numbers and solfege syllables (like do, re, mi) as text. Glass also knew that the musicians could not play continuously for such a long time. He divided the ensemble into groups that alternate with one another. Only occasionally does the group play all together.

In composing the music for *Einstein on the Beach* Glass used two techniques that he developed when writing *Music in Twelve Parts*. The first technique is called additive process, in which Glass starts with a group of notes which he repeats several times. He then adds one note to the group and repeats that. He adds another note to the group and repeats that, and so on. Glass also uses this method in reverse. He subtracts one note from the group after each repetition. In this manner, a simple figure can get longer or shorter in many different ways, depending on what note is added or subtracted. As the figure is altered it takes on many different rhythmic shapes.

The other device Glass developed and uses is cyclic structure. For this, he plays several rhythmic patterns at once, each of a different length. After the patterns are repeated over and over, they eventually arrive back at their starting points, all at the same time. This completes one cycle. Some writers have described this process as sounding like little wheels turning inside big wheels. This is a type of polymeter, meaning "many meters," going on at once.

Glass uses his cyclic structure for the opening train scene in *Einstein on the Beach*. The cyclic structure is reflected visually by the train wheels. In this music, the upper part repeated three times is equal in length to the lower part repeated four times.

While creating their opera, Wilson and Glass also had to find producers who were willing to finance it. They knew they would have to look for European backers. The U.S. government provides very little money for the arts and large American corporations usually ignore the avant-garde. In contrast, nearly every major European city hosts annual music and theater festivals that are almost entirely government funded.

A tour of *Einstein on the Beach* was eventually arranged. It lasted four months and included thirty performances in six countries: France, Italy, Germany, Yugloslavia, Holland, and Belgium. The premiere took place at the Avignon Festival in France.

The *Einstein* tour was a huge success. Some fanatical fans followed the company around Europe, attending performances as many times as they could. In Paris, two hundred people stood outside the theater on the chance that people might leave early and give them ticket stubs.

Philip Glass at the keyboard
Richard Pasley; *used by permission from* Keyboard Magazine

As the *Einstein* company moved from city to city,
minor changes were made. Glass's children, Juliet and
Zachary, then eight and five, joined the company in
Italy for three weeks. Rather than leave them with a
babysitter, Glass had Wilson create small parts for
them in the opera so that he could keep an eye on
them during the performance.

Back in the U.S., producers were working on a plan
to bring *Einstein* to the Metropolitan Opera House as a
special event. When arrangements were finally made,
Glass worried that the four thousand seats in the house

might be only half-filled. He was surprised when both of the performances sold out. Word about *Einstein* had traveled to the United States from Europe.

When the opera closed, Glass' producers were faced with a debt of $90,000. They had lost $10,000 per night at the Metropolitan Opera House, even though they had sold all the tickets they had. This is a common problem in opera. Even traditional operas lose money because they are so expensive to produce.

After the excitement of *Einstein* was all over, Glass returned to his job as a taxi driver. One day a well-dressed woman got into his cab. New York law requires that each cab driver posts his photograph and name in the car and this caught the woman's attention. She leaned forward in her seat, and said, "Young man, do you realize you have the same name as a very famous composer?" Fortunately, after another three years, Glass was able to support himself solely by composing and playing his music.

The music Glass wrote before *Einstein on the Beach* was called radical because he used very few changes in harmony and melody. After a while, he realized that if he continued to keep harmony and melody static, his pieces would all sound alike. Glass remembers thinking, "I noticed that I had been operating under a lot of rules that had become automatic, and that there were things that weren't possible to do in my music because I had made them forbidden. I said, 'Why can't I do it? Well, there's this rule. Rule!!? Who's making the rules? I'm making the rules.' and that was the end of the rule."

Glass then spent the next ten years solving the problem of combining harmonic progression with rhythmic structure. As he worked out his new ideas in harmony, his music began to sound quite different than his earlier works. This change is obvious in his next two operas, *Satyagraha* and *Akhnaten*. These works also differ from *Einstein* in that they are written for full orchestra and operatic voices.

Satyagraha is based on Mohandas Gandhi and his struggle against racial discrimination in South Africa. *Satyagraha*, which means "the firmness of truth," is the name Gandhi gave to his nonviolent movement. His peaceful demonstrations brought religious and political freedom to his countrymen. *Satyagraha* is sung in Sanskrit, the ancient language of India. The text is taken from the sacred book of the Hindu religion, the *Bhagavad-Gita*.

In seeking his subject for his third opera, Glass went way back in time to 1300 B.C. Akhnaten was an Egyptian pharaoh who may have been the first person to believe in one God. He tried to force his people to worship one God instead of many different ones.

Glass calls *Einstein on the Beach*, *Satyagraha*, and *Akhnaten* "portrait" operas because they are centered around historical figures. Einstein represents science, Gandhi is a figure of political action, and Akhnaten depicts religion. Glass thinks of them as "three people who changed history through the force of their inner vision, through simply having an idea. They changed the world completely."

Glass has written many other operas, including *The*

Juniper Tree; The Making of the Representative for Planet 8, based on the science fiction novel by Doris Lessing; *The Fall of the House of Usher,* based on the story by Edgar Allan Poe; and *A Thousand Airplanes,* a science-fiction music drama written for the Philip Glass Ensemble and one actor.

Besides his opera, Glass has composed a lot of other music. He wrote six pieces specifically for his album, *Glassworks,* released in 1982. One cut on the album is a five-minute piece called "Floe." A floe is a sheet of ice floating on water. The composition opens with a slowly repeated figure in the wind instruments. The electronic keyboard bursts into fast rippling chords, called arpeggios, which have become one of Glass's trademarks. Another keyboard joins in, and then another, playing different rhythms. The wind instruments also contribute new figures and rhythms to the texture. Horns abruptly blast out sustained, accented tones. Layer by layer, the sound is stacked, making the music busy and vibrant. Listening carefully, you can hear Glass's techniques of additive process and cyclic structure.

As the piece progresses, new rhythms are introduced, and others are dropped. Changes are gradual, but Glass always provides plenty to listen to. The pulsing music grows in volume and intensity, then suddenly breaks off. The slow opening theme returns. Again the keyboard and wind parts are layered on, but at a slower rhythm. The movement accelerates and the ascent begins again. This time the music drives even harder toward the climax. At its peak, the music abruptly stops.

For his recording project, *Songs From Liquid Days*, Glass collaborated with popular artists Paul Simon, David Bryne, Laurie Anderson, and Suzanne Vega. He thought these pop songwriters could teach him something about setting texts. Anderson and Vega contributed finished lyrics, but Simon's and Byrne's songs evolved as Glass wrote the music. As Simon heard his song *Changing Opinion*, in various stages, he changed phrasing and words. He revised it so many times that his final choice for a title, "Song with Refrigerator in It" didn't make the printing deadline. Many artists perform on the album, including the Philip Glass Ensemble, the Kronos String Quartet, Linda Ronstadt, and The Roches.

Composers who write serious music aren't supposed to work with pop artists, but that doesn't bother Glass. "I don't see why I shouldn't. It seems that I only have one chance to do this, so I'm interested in looking into it all." This attitude has made Philip Glass unusually successful in both the classified and pop music worlds.

SUGGESTED LISTENING

MILTON BABBITT
Columbia-Princeton Electronic Music Center
"Composition for Synthesizer"
Columbia Masterworks

Music for Virtuosos
"Phoemena" for soprano and tape
New World NW-209

HENRY COWELL
Piano Music of Henry Cowell
Henry Cowell, pianist
Folkways FM-3349

GEORGE CRUMB
Ancient Voices of Children
Elektra/Nonesuch 79149-2

Vox Balaenae ("Voice of the Whale")
for electric flue, electric cello, and electric piano
New World NW-357-2

GEORGE GERSHWIN
Porgy and Bess
Houston Grand Opera Company
RCA RCD3-2109

Rhapsody in Blue
Leonard Bernstein (pianist and conductor) and the Columbia Symphony
CBS MLK-39454

PHILIP GLASS
Glassworks
Philip Glass Ensemble
CBS MK-37265

Tehillim
Steve Reich and Musicians
ECM/Warner Brothers 827411-2

Songs from Liquid Days
Lyrics by Laurie Anderson, David Byrne, Paul Simon, and Suzanne Vega
Philip Glass Ensemble
CBS MK-39564

LOUIS MOREAU GOTTSCHALK
Piano Music
List, pianist.
Vanguard VCD-72026

CHARLES IVES
Holidays Symphony
Michael Tilson Thomas conducts the Chicago Symphony
CBS MK-42381

Songs
Roberta Alexander, soprano
Etcetera KTC-1020

EDWARD MACDOWELL
Sea Pieces and *Woodland Sketches*
Fierro, pianist
Nonesuch 71411

Suite No. 2, Op. 48 "Indian"
Howard Hanson conducts the Eastman-Rochester Orchestra
Mercury 75026 PSI

STEVE REICH
Different Trains
Kronos Quartet
Electric Counterpoint
Pat Metheny, electric guitar
Elektra/Nonesuch 79176-2

RUTH CRAWFORD SEEGER
String Quartet
Composers Quartet
Nonesuch 71280

FOR FURTHER READING

An American Rhapsody: The Story of George Gershwin by Paul Kresh (Lodestar/Dutton, 1988)

Contributions of Women: Music By Catherine Scheader (Dillon Press, 1985)

Introduction to Contemporary Music by Joseph Machlis (W.W. Norton, 1979)

Music by Philip Glass by Philip Glass (Harper and Row, 1988)

Music's Connecticut Yankee: An Introduction to the Life and Music of Charles Ives by Helen Sive Paxton (Atheneum, 1977)

Notes of a Pianist by Louis Moreau Gottschalk (Knopf, 1964)

Profile of a Composer: George Crumb edited by Don Gillespie (C. F. Peters Corporation, 1986)

Writings about Music by Steve Reich (New York University Press, 1974)

GLOSSARY

absolute music Instrumental music that does not tell a story or describe a scene; the opposite of program music.

accompaniment The part of the music that supports the main melody or soloist.

alto A low female voice.

articulation The manner of attacking and releasing a note.

avant-garde Artists and musicians who experiment with new art forms which are not usually understood or accepted by the general public.

bass A low male voice.

bebop A type of jazz developed in the 1940s that is usually played by a small group of musicians.

blues A folk and jazz style with flatted notes. Lyrics of blues songs are usually about unhappiness or bad luck.

bitonality Using two keys at once that usually clash with each other.

canon Two or more voices or instruments playing the same melody at the same time, only starting at different times. For example, a round like "Row, row, row your boat" is a type of canon.

chamber music Compositions for one or a few musicians which can be played in a room in a house rather than a concert hall.

chord Combination of three or more notes sounded together.

choreography A set of steps and movements for dancers.

coda The ending of a musical composition.

concerto A large composition, for orchestra and solo instrument, usually divided into three movements.

conservatory A music school.

consonance Combined tones that create a feeling of rest. The opposite of dissonance.

counterpoint Two or more melodies played at once.

cross-rhythms   Two or more rhythmic patterns going on at the same time, such as groups of three and groups of four.

dissonance   Combined tones that clash, creating restlessness. The opposite of consonance.

dominant   The fifth note or chord in a scale.

downbeat   The first and strongest beat in a measure.

duple meter   Two beats per measure.

dynamics   The volume of music, from very loud to very soft.

ensemble   A group of musicians.

ethnomusicologist   One who studies folk music and music of different countries and cultures.

folk music   Music that consists mostly of songs, created by people who have no musical training, and usually passed down from generation to generation without being written down.

glissando   A rapid slide up or down a scale.

harmonic progression   The way chords follow one another.

harmonics   On stringed instruments, a high flutelike tone produced by lightly touching a string instead of pressing it all the way down.

harmony   Chords that support the melody. The study of music which deals with how chords are formed and how they follow each other.

improvise   To make up music at the same time it is being performed.

interval   The distance between two notes on a musical staff or two keys on a piano. For example, two keys next to each other would be a small interval or step, two keys with five or six keys in between them would be a large interval or leap.

inversion   In twelve-tone music, an interval reversed or turned upside down so that its mirror image is created. For example, the inversion of C up four piano keys to F would be C down four piano keys to G.

jazz   A style of music that is usually improvised or made up on the spot, with syncopated rhythms, developed in the United

States, predominantly by black musicians, in the first half of the twentieth century.

key The most important note, chord, and scale of a composition.

legato Smooth, flowing sounds which are not interrupted by silences. The opposite of staccato.

libretto The text of an opera.

lyricist One who writes the words of a song.

lyrics The words of a song.

measure A rhythmic group containing a certain number of beats marked off on a score by vertical lines.

meter A group of beats, in which the first one is strongest.

minimalist music A style of music with a strong beat, many repetitions of short melodies, and few changes in dynamics and harmony, developed in the 1960s.

modulation A change of key within a composition.

monster-concert A performance involving an unusually large number of musicians.

motive A short musical idea that is developed throughout a composition.

movement A part of a large composition that has its own melodic, rhythmic, and harmonic structure.

multi-movement A composition that has more than one movement, usually performed with pauses between the movements.

musicologist One who studies music and music history.

nationalistic composer A composer who uses the folk songs, dances, legends, and other national material of his homeland in his music.

notate To write down a musical idea.

notation System of writing down music.

opus Latin word for "work." A number which tells in which order a composer's work was published; Abbreviation: op.

orchestration Arranging a composition for orchestra. Choosing which instruments will play each part of the music.

perfect pitch   The ability to identify any pitch by ear.

piece   A composition that is played on musical instruments.

pizzicato   A way to play stringed instruments in which the strings are plucked.

prodigy   A very talented child.

program music   Music that tells a story or describes a scene. The opposite of absolute music.

quadruple meter   Four beats per measure.

quarter tones   Pitches that exist in between half steps. Since piano keyboards are built in half steps, quarter tones can not be played on them.

ragtime   A style of jazz, developed in the 1890s, usually for solo piano, usually in duple meter, with a march-like tempo.

rhapsody   A free-form musical composition.

register   Part of the total range of a musical instrument or voice. For example, a register could be described as low, mid-range, or high.

retrograde   Beginning with the last note of a musical idea and rewriting it backwards to the first note.

scale   The notes of a key, ordered from the lowest to the highest.

score   The written version of a musical composition.

serialism   Another word for twelve-tone music; sometimes used as another word for total serialism.

sonata   A composition for solo instrument which often includes a piano accompaniment.

song   A composition that is sung.

soprano   A high female voice.

staccato   Short, detached notes, with silences in between. The opposite of legato.

storyboard   Sketches of scenes for a opera or musical created when the production is in the early planning stage.

string quartet   An ensemble which includes two violins, one viola, and one cello. A composition written for string quartet.

suite   A set of short pieces, having related subject matter.

symphony   A composition written for orchestra. An orchestra.

syncopation   Accenting a note at an unexpected time, as on a weak beat or between two beats.

tempo   At what speed a composition is played.

tenor   A high male voice.

theme   A melody that is used several times within a movement or composition.

theory   The study of the structure of music including rhythm, melody, harmony, form, ear training, style, counterpoint, and orchestration.

timbre   Quality of sound that makes one instrument or voice sound different from another. Also called tone color.

tonality   The most widely-used system for organizing musical materials from 1700 to the present.

tone clusters   Chords made up of many notes spaced very close together.

tone row   Another name for twelve-tone music.

tonic   The first note or chord of a scale.

total serialism   Method of composing in which the elements of music—pitch, rhythm, dynamics, timbre—are ordered in a group or series. An extension of twelve-tone music.

transcribe   To notate or write down on paper music that already exists.

transpose   To change music from one key to another.

twelve-tone music   A system for organizing musical materials in which all twelve tones are treated equally, invented by composer Arnold Schoenberg in the 1920s to replace the traditional system of tonality.

virtuosic   An adjective used to describe a very difficult musical composition.

virtuoso   A highly skilled musician.

word painting   In songs, music that represents an image in the lyrics. For example, fast notes sung on the word, "running," or one person singing on the word, "alone."

INDEX

219